C000181585

The Racial Code

The Racial Code
Tales of Resistance and Survival

NICOLA ROLLOCK

ALLEN LANE
an imprint of
PENGUIN BOOKS

ALLEN LANE

UK | USA | Canada | Ireland | Australia
India | New Zealand | South Africa

Penguin Books is part of the Penguin Random House group of companies
whose addresses can be found at global.penguinrandomhouse.com.

Penguin
Random House
UK

First published by Allen Lane 2022
001

Set in 12.5/15pt Garamond MT Std
Typeset by Jouve (UK), Milton Keynes
Printed and bound in Great Britain by Clays Ltd, Elcograf S.p.A.

The authorized representative in the EEA is Penguin Random House Ireland,
Morrison Chambers, 32 Nassau Street, Dublin D02 YH68

A CIP catalogue record for this book is available from the British Library

ISBN: 978–0–241–52105–2

www.greenpenguin.co.uk

To the Elders – passed and present – who have been
fighting the cause long before I was born and
who paved the way for generations yet to come.

What they see is a disastrous, continuing, present, condition which menaces them, and for which they bear an inescapable responsibility. But since, in the main, they seem to lack the energy to change this condition, they would rather not be reminded of it.

James Baldwin, *Dark Days*

Contents

Introduction 1
A Brief Note on Terminology 17

1: Acts of a Lone Woman 19
Part I: Tap Shoes 19
Part II: The Oracle 24

2: The Meeting 37

Interlude: How Many Times? 53

3: Members Only 57

4: 'Keep A-Knocking But You Can't Come In' 70

Interlude: Committed to Equality & Diversity 89

5: The Christmas Party 91

6: V.O.Y.E.U.R. 108

Interlude: Can I Be Your White Bitch? 125

7: Nigel's Story 128

8: A Special Kind of Madness — 150

    Scenario 1 – The Engagement Party — 150

    Scenario 2 – The Wheels on the Bus — 153

    Scenario 3 – The Letter of Complaint — 156

    A guide to writing an institutional response to a charge of racism — 161

Interlude: The Facemask — 166

9: Default to White — 171

10: Darker Than Blue — 185

Discussion: The Persistence of the Racial Code — 197

    Breaking the First Rule — 200

    What White People Really Know about Race — 207

    The Emperor's New Clothes — 211

Endnotes — 215

References — 246

Acknowledgements — 257

Introduction

I was at university when I heard about his murder.

I was in my second year of a Psychology degree and was struggling to cope with university life. There were three key anxieties that preoccupied me during that time: money, alcohol and race. The money part was straightforward. I didn't have any. I didn't come from a wealthy background and was struggling – despite the system of grants available at the time – to make ends meet. I took on every conceivable part-time job I could to support myself throughout my degree. I learnt to shop on the most meagre of budgets, split an apple so that it served breakfast and lunch and had a penny jar that was more often empty than full.

My experience of alcohol, prior to joining university, was limited. There were the empty glasses left over from when my dad's friends visited our modest home in a quiet corner of southwest London, but those glasses served as the background accompaniment to long debates about politics 'back home', to fast-paced jokes that my child's ear never quite caught the drift of, and to the loud slamming of dominoes on our dining room table. Yes, alcohol was available at the house parties and clubs I went to in my late teens, but its presence was a mere backdrop to the night. My friends and I went out for the music, to dance and to check out boys. Suddenly, at university, alcohol was everywhere. It was the central vehicle through which to meet others and, apparently, the central ingredient to enjoying oneself. Even the term 'pub crawl' had to be explained to me.

I didn't understand. I felt alienated. Along with the few other Black girls at the University of Liverpool in the 1990s, I had to suffer drunk white students (and the odd Black or South Asian one) dancing wildly and disjointedly to music on one of the few club nights in the month that played the RnB and hip hop tunes we liked. The opening bars of House of Pain's 'Jump Around' came to serve as our signal to exit the dance floor as quickly as possible before those same drunk students began jumping with near full pints in their hands, showering all in their range with cheap booze.

It was also while at university that I began to think properly about race. Even my predominantly white independent girls' school in south London had not prepared me for what university would reveal to me. I met a white guy on my course and, brought together by a love of food, theatre and books, we started dating. Race soon made itself known, and it was not as a consequence of his love of The Smiths and The Cure compared with my love of En Vogue and Jodeci. Race arrived silently and unexpectedly in the condemning gaze and unkind remarks of Black male peers who, like me, were part of the African Caribbean Society. Somehow by deciding to date a white guy I was insulting and rejecting them. I was confused. Did this mean that I was also rejecting part of myself since we shared the same brown skin? I had not realized that my choice of boyfriend was a public and political act and not merely a personal one. And for many in my boyfriend's family, I was the first young Black woman they had ever met. This idea – of being the first – also confused me. What kind of lives had they led that meant they had so far only managed to meet other white people? I struggled to envisage that world. Odd questions were asked of me about who I was and about who my family were, as if they were trying to ascertain my legitimacy, my right to exist. I felt awkward and seen for all the wrong reasons. And as if this was not enough to contend with, when my then boyfriend and I dared venture down the streets of Liverpool, brown hand clasped in white, we were frequently met with the cutting looks of strangers who slowed down sufficiently in their cars to make sure we were soaked in their verbal bile.

It was against this backdrop that I made the acquaintance of the white guy on the floor above me in halls whose hip hop repertoire and style of street dress extended far beyond any Black guy I had ever known. It was as a result of his friendliness that I learnt about Public Enemy. I listened avidly; every word, every beat, every pause of *Rebirth of a Nation* nourishing my famished soul. And it was somewhere amidst Flavour Flav et al. and the literary excellence of Maya Angelou, Zora Neale Hurston, Toni Morrison and Alex Haley's *The Autobiography of Malcolm X* that I began to understand that my confusions, my soul-searching, were not isolated endeavours. I began to understand myself as racialized, as having historicity. I began to understand that, in line with what I had experienced at university, a world existed where the colour of your skin marked you out as different and shaped how others viewed you. In short, I began to make sense of and negotiate an existence from a place that I would later come to understand as 'the margins'.[1]

It was while working out who I was, what race was, what Black identity was, who white people were and their role in this, that I heard the news about the murder.

A young Black boy – about my age – had been stabbed to death in south London.

His name was Stephen Lawrence.

The suspects were five white youths, but they had not yet been arrested even though the police had been advised of their names. Stephen had simply been waiting for a bus with a friend and was murdered because of the colour of his skin. My mind was numb with incomprehension, with an inability to assign logic or reason to what the news insisted on telling me. Racism had resulted in the loss of life. Racism had resulted in the loss of life of someone who looked like me and it had happened on the streets of London, right here in the UK. And while I had a vague awareness of the 1981 Brixton riots and other important moments of British racial discord, the books in which I had found solace had been largely about America; they were about a world I saw on the TV, a world that was far away. It was a world similar to but different from my own. Yet, here was the news telling me that such terrible deeds were possible on the very streets of London, the only other city I knew as well as Liverpool at that time.

And if I needed any confirmation of the horror that had occurred, it came just a few weeks after Stephen Lawrence's murder. While on a visit to the UK, Nelson Mandela proclaimed to a still shocked nation: 'The Lawrence tragedy is our tragedy. I am deeply touched by the brutality of the murder – brutality that we are all used to in South Africa, where black lives are cheap.'[2] Black life was clearly also cheap in a non-apartheid UK where, in addition to Stephen's murder, the subsequent police handling of the case would leave me pained, incensed and dumbfounded. I couldn't fathom what his family must have been going through.

The year was 1993. I didn't know then that Stephen Lawrence and the wider case, which would span more than twenty years, would become a key part of my life and inform how I came to make sense of and theorize race and racism.

*

Fifteen years later, with a PhD under my belt, I won a commission from the influential race equality think tank the Runnymede Trust. The brief was to carry out the first ever independent review of the government's progress in meeting the seventy recommendations of the Stephen Lawrence Inquiry report completed by Sir William Macpherson and his three advisers.[3] The Inquiry had sought to identify 'the matters arising from the death of Stephen Lawrence [...] in order particularly to identify the lessons to be learned for the investigation and prosecution of racially motivated crimes'. The first hearing of the Inquiry took place in October 1997. As well as written submissions, it took evidence from eighty-eight witnesses. The report, comprising of two volumes, was eventually published in 1999. It concluded:

> There is no doubt that there were fundamental errors. The investigation was marred by a combination of professional incompetence, institutional racism and a failure of leadership by senior officers. A flawed Metropolitan Police review failed to expose these inadequacies. The second investigation could not salvage the faults of the first investigation.
>
> William Macpherson (1999: column 390)

In a watershed moment in UK race relations, the Stephen Lawrence Inquiry report introduced the term 'institutional racism' to a mainstream audience, drawing attention to the ways in which racism against Black and minority ethnic groups could be 'unwitting' and evidenced in processes, policies and procedures that lead to unequal outcomes and experiences for these groups.[4]

I had just six months to establish whether Macpherson's recommendations had, in fact, been implemented as my findings needed to be ready in time for the Inquiry report's ten-year anniversary in February 2009.

Those six months had a profound impact on me.

I reviewed every conceivable publication – government, academic, voluntary sector and otherwise. I analysed Section 95 statistics, interviewed Doreen Lawrence, the mother of the murdered teenager, attended meetings at the Home Office in order to establish whether each recommendation had been met.[5] I learnt and became familiar with police terminology and their ranks as I examined data on recruitment, promotion and progression. I became absorbed by the data and arguments surrounding stop and search. I learnt about family liaison officers, senior investigating officers and spoke with countless individuals – lawyers, policymakers, police officers and academics – in order to help me meet the objectives of the review.

What I found stunned me.

While there had been considerable progress in meeting the majority of the recommendations, gaps remained in relation to one area: race. I recall sitting at my desk in Runnymede's offices in Liverpool Street unable to comprehend what I had found. I checked and rechecked figures. I asked my Runnymede colleagues to read what I had written. I spoke again to statisticians and analysts. It was true. Despite the funding that had been made available to support local and national race equality projects and initiatives, despite changes in legislation, despite the fact that at the time debate about institutional racism was commonplace across the media, there had been near to no change in relation to those recommendations that pertained to race over the ten-year period between 1999 and 2009.[6] The number of Black and minority ethnic officers retained and promoted across the forty-three police forces was as depressingly low in 2009 as it had been ten years earlier. In fact, the government had abandoned targets put in place to increase the recruitment of these officers even though several forces had failed to meet them and even though, in some cases, it would have meant recruiting just one officer.[7] And, as I noted at the time, the trends surrounding stop and search were no more uplifting. Statistics indicated that Black groups continued to be disproportionately stopped and searched at rates similar to when the Stephen Lawrence Inquiry report was published a decade earlier in 1999. Further, I learnt that only a low percentage of these stops actually resulted in arrest let alone conviction. This led me to conclude that there was little substantive difference between these procedures and the discriminatory 'sus laws' of the 1970s, and that stop and search was not the most effective use of police time and resources.[8]

I had expected and quietly hoped for change. It didn't make sense. How was it possible that, despite the law, and despite the political attention and oft-vocalized commitment for change, scant progress had been made in relation to those recommendations that centred on race? The question weighed heavily on me for months.

The political response did not assuage my concerns. In February 2009, at a major conference to mark ten years since the publication of the Stephen Lawrence Inquiry report arranged jointly by the Ministry of Justice, the Home Office and the National Policing Improvement Agency, the message from senior leaders seemed to contradict what the data showed. For example, two days before the conference, the then Secretary of State for Justice Jack Straw played down the idea that institutional racism continued to have any relevance in Britain. Speaking on BBC News, Straw insisted that only 'pockets' of institutional racism remained.[9] Years later, Straw would clarify to me that this statement did not mean that the matter had been fully resolved.[10] At the conference itself the then Metropolitan Police Commissioner Sir Paul Stephenson was unequivocal: 'I no longer believe the label [of institutional racism] to be either appropriate or useful', much to the discernible consternation of members of the National Black Police Association in attendance.[11] And the then Chair of the Equality and Human Rights Commission Trevor Phillips denounced the use of the term 'institutional racism' altogether, arguing instead for what he positioned as the more all-encompassing term 'systemic bias'.[12]

I watched these events unfold with curiosity and concern. Could we really claim that institutional racism had ended any more than we could claim that, say, sexism had definitively ended? What about the evidence? What about the government's own data? It did not make sense. What lay behind the claims of these high-profile, influential individuals?

Ten years later in January 2019, following a career as an academic, I was appointed Specialist Adviser to the government's Home Affairs Select Committee inquiry 'The Macpherson Report: Twenty-one years on'. The role pulled me into a key part of the parliamentary process, advising a cross-party selection of MPs who comprised the Committee on the direction that the Inquiry should take, which witnesses to call and the questions that should be asked of them. It was as though I'd been thrown back in time. The accounts of racial disproportionality and discrimination were the same as in previous years and as I had documented in my own research for the Runnymede Trust. So too were the frustrations of the Black and minority ethnic groups – be they police officers, activists or lawyers – who came to give evidence. White colleagues who specialized in equalities and human rights were also frustrated. And the attempts by senior white leaders who came before the Committee to explain and justify the continued problems were also the same. Like so many others who had come before them, they too made sincere promises, expressed their *personal* commitment, and emphasized how *very* seriously they took the matter of what was now being described as 'diversity and inclusion'.

So why, given the supposed sincerity of these commitments, the legislation, the policies and guidance, had so little changed when it came to race and racism? Why were the same patterns of racial inequality evident? Why had my concerns about how we respond to racism, triggered when I was at university, not abated? There had to be something we were overlooking that would help make sense of the continued racial inequalities.

That something was a rulebook: a racial code that documents the rules that govern our lives.

In *The Racial Code* I argue that mainstream perceptions of racism are wrong and overly preoccupied with explicit or extreme forms of racism seen to exist only on the fringes of society. Instead, I draw attention to the existence of more subtle forms of racism which saturate everyday life and shape interactions between (and sometimes within) different racialized groups. These interactions help determine who is seen to belong, who is included and excluded from different social spaces and roles, and, crucially, help maintain a racial status quo where white people remain at the top of the hierarchy and people of colour are at the bottom. This racism

makes itself known through racial microaggressions, stereotyping and policies that proclaim an adherence to equalities,
but which instead embed and even rationalize worse outcomes and poorer experiences for Black and minority ethnic
groups. *The Racial Code* reveals why, despite commitments
from policymakers and leaders to change, despite legislation,
the policy documents and the recent trend for diversity and
inclusion and unconscious bias training, efforts to meaning-
fully advance racial justice remain unfulfilled.[13]

Almost everyone has an opinion about race and racism. As a
Black woman, the conversations I have about race with most
Black and Asian peers are fundamentally different from those
I have with most white people because we enter the conversation with different investments, different experiences of
race and racism, different racialized identities and ambitions.
And our racialized identities are predicated on historical
norms and societal expectations that shape our very viewpoint of the world.[14] As such, talking to white people about
race and racism is a tricky, if not risky affair which often
exposes the very behaviours that help to keep racism intact.[15]
White people often become defensive or deny that racism is
a determining factor when the subject is raised. Sometimes
this denial takes the form of anger and sometimes it takes
on the guise of reasoned intellectual debate. It matters little
that they themselves have no first-hand knowledge of what
it is like to be racially minoritized or indeed what it is to personally suffer racism based on the colour of their skin alone.
Despite this, they continue to control the principles and rules
of race, demanding from people of colour judicial levels of
evidence about the salience of racism whose validity only
they as white people can approve.[16] This can be seen across every

aspect of society and reflects a pattern of power that white people maintain even if they state ambitions and arguments to the contrary. *The Racial Code* reveals how structural inequalities of race with which we are all now mostly familiar, such as data showing the underrepresentation of senior Black employees, are upheld by micro-level or local acts of racial exclusion.

As stated, white people do not have to live with racism or suffer its consequences based on the colour of their skin alone.[17] That is, their skin does not mark them out as a problem to be surveyed, monitored, assessed, regulated or even killed. As a result, they can be regarded as privileged.[18] They are able to navigate society – walk down the street without fear of the police, not worry to the same extent about school exclusions or not being promoted, or the possibility of dying in childbirth – without having to consider that the colour of their skin might cause a problem and without having to determine how to achieve and survive despite this. And because of the legacy of colonialism and their larger number in the global north, white people are in a position of power when it comes to race. This does not necessarily only mean that they hold financial, economic or political power. This might be true, but not all white people are wealthy or in positions of leadership. Racial power refers to the ability to shape the racial status quo. It refers to the ability to dictate which norms and whose culture will be given a platform for example, taught in schools, depicted in museums, reported in the news. It includes how the law is interpreted and enacted and who is seen as normal, 'one of us', or aberrant, different, odd. In short, white people hold and enact racial power and people of colour are the subjects of it. Today, it is commonly agreed that there is no such thing as race. That is, the idea of distinct racial groups marked by genetic differences has been found to be without basis, though, of course, historically it served as justification for the dehumanizing treatment of Africans during the Transatlantic Slave Trade and of Jewish people during the Holocaust. However, the idea of racial difference is still very much with us and it is this that keeps alive the notion of distinct racial groups and continues to give fuel to racism.[19] This is evidenced through processes, decisions and behaviours which reinforce particular tropes about racial difference and, in so doing, reveal patterns of racial power in seemingly innocuous interactions that shape the very fabric of our society.

The chapters that follow are presented as a series of narratives or vignettes formed by drawing together a range of sources including empirical research evidence, theoretical arguments, statistical data and news items as well as accounts shared with me during the course of my professional career. I am fully aware that, as an academic, sometimes our ways of communicating whether in spoken or written form can be alienating, theoretically dense and primarily only resonate with other academics. And, as a Black scholar interested in racial justice, there is an inherent contradiction in framing arguments to be consumed predominantly by the elitist world of the academy. The racial justice project necessarily includes but also extends beyond that space, and the particular form of storytelling used throughout this book provides a visceral means of communicating with a wider audience.

As such, I engage a tool which gives voice to people of colour and centres their experiences. *Counternarratives* (sometimes referred to as *chronicles*) challenge that which is traditionally presented as the mainstream and instead offer a perspective and analysis that is shaped by the viewpoint and experiences of racially minoritized groups. *Narrative* refers to the idea of storytelling and *counter* denotes the idea of challenging that which is traditionally presented as the norm.[20] To put this in context, my experiences as a Black person and those of many others meant that we were not shocked into a moment of 'awakening' following the murder of George Floyd as I have heard many white people describe their reaction. Instead, Floyd's murder, in May 2020, at the knee of a white police officer represented for many of us the sickening end of a continuum of experiences that are almost an unremarkable part of our everyday existence. It is this 'outgroup' perspective and experience that I draw attention to in the pages that follow while also revealing how it is shaped by the rules and dynamics of those who continue to occupy positions of power.

Counternarrative is one of the tools of Critical Race Theory (CRT). Although Critical Race Theory has been subject to criticism by certain politicians and commentators on both sides of the Atlantic, those debates have been founded on erroneous and dangerous misinterpretations of what is, in fact, an academic theoretical lens to help make sense of unexplained racial disparities and racism.[21] CRT was first developed in the US, in the 1970s, by scholars of colour concerned about the absence of a critical examination of race within legal scholarship.[22] It is based on an understanding that racial inequalities are the consequence of assumptions, social norms and power relations which hold firm beyond stated ambitions for racial equality. CRT scholars reveal how relatively unremarkable everyday behaviours and practices uphold inequitable outcomes for racially minoritized groups through the way in which policies and processes are rationalized, organized or structured.[23] For example, the underrepresentation of Black employees at senior levels is often attributed to being a problem of progression through the pipeline. This serves to detract from a more complex analysis that also examines racial disparities in workplace experiences and outcomes concerning, for example, grievances, redundancies and resignations that impact on staff retention irrespective of their having entered the system. CRT scholars are interested in these gaps in analysis and their consequences.[24]

It is not my intention to present, in this book, a simplistic binary case of white people bad, people of colour good. I will show how those racialized as white benefit from racism whereas people of colour do not. However, I also seek to examine the complexity and fluidity of racism and to show how white people can also undermine the rules of *The Racial Code* in order to treat racially minoritized groups equitably and advance an anti-racism agenda. Conversely, people of colour can embody, enact and espouse the very racial rules upheld by those racialized as white in a way that grants them (temporary) access to and acceptance within predominantly white spaces.

Breaking from standard non-fiction convention and in line with the traditions of counternarrative, I make extensive use of endnotes throughout the book as a way of speaking to and guiding the reader. These endnotes offer insight into the academic arguments which sit behind the stories and, as such, provide references, statistical evidence and an overview of theoretical concepts so that the reader can delve deeper into the thinking underpinning the points should they wish.[25] Some chapters conclude by offering comment and analysis of key arguments and themes. Elsewhere, this analysis is carried out by characters within the body of the narrative.

The chapters are interspersed by four interludes. Their

brevity is deliberate and meant to reveal how moments of racist othering and exclusion can indeed be cursory or fleeting but nonetheless affect the course of the day, the feelings and well-being of racially minoritized people while also revealing how those racialized as white – and those who share their perspective – view the world, view racism and view us. Such incidents might include a momentary exchange when paying for goods or an apparent throw-away remark from a white neighbour. No matter how fleeting, they each help us understand the dynamics of the racial code.

The counternarratives should be understood as providing a glimpse into an incident or event as opposed to being an in-depth fictional short story. I sometimes make use of satire and, on occasion, parody, in order to emphasize the tensions and contradictions in the ways in which we hold on to race even while pretending it does not matter. And there are moments in which the boundary between a presented reality and the use of these literary tools is opaque. This is a calculated ploy precisely to embed the reader within the murky confusions and second-guessing that racism foists upon its subjects.

While the complexity of racial arguments is designed to increase within each chapter, there is no need to read them in sequence. Each stands alone but also sits in complement to the others. Characters make an appearance at different points throughout the book in order to draw attention to the various roles and relationships we have to race and also to emphasize how, particularly for people of colour, the enactment of race is very much shaped by proximity to white people and to whiteness.

I invite the reader to ask questions of the text, the characters and themselves throughout. For example:

- Who is speaking and how? What is the context in which they are speaking? How do others respond to them?
- If the character had not spoken, what would you infer about the kind of person they might be, for example, via their appearance and how others respond to them?
- If a character appears in more than one chapter, do they come across altogether different or are they the same? If different, what (based on the information available) might have influenced a change in their manner?
- How is the person's character shaped by their racial identity, gender or class position?
- If these were to be substituted (for example, the white woman becomes a white man or the white man becomes a Black man), how might the scene play out differently?
- Do you recognize aspects of yourself in the text? How does this make you feel? How does your understanding of your racial identity and experiences shape what you are reading?[26]
- Are there particular moments in the chapters that annoy or provoke you or cause discomfort? Why might this be?
- Conversely, are there incidents that stimulate warmth and empathy? Why?
- Can you relate to any of the incidents? What has the chapter or incident taught you about race and racism?
- Have you been in a similar situation? If so, how did you react or what might you now do differently?

A Brief Note on Terminology

The language used to talk about race is important. It provides a vehicle through which to make sense of, draw attention to or counter common tropes about racial difference and injustice and the processes that keep it intact. As readers work their way through the book, they will observe that I sometimes make use of widely recognized terminology *Black, Asian and minority ethnic* people. However, for the most part, I use the term *racially minoritized* to refer to these groups and *racialized as white* to refer to white people. I was introduced to this language by Black British scholars working with communities who faced multiple levels of discrimination and disadvantage. I find these terms helpful because they draw attention to process. For example, to describe myself as *racialized as Black* acknowledges that the colour of my skin has meanings inscribed on to it by mainstream white society which, in turn, shapes how I am viewed and treated.[1] Similarly, *racialized as white* refers to the process through which white people have been socialized or learnt to act in ways associated with their group to the disadvantage of minoritized populations.

1: Acts of a Lone Woman

Part I: Tap Shoes

Racial battle fatigue develops in African American and other people of colour much like combat fatigue in military personnel, even when they are not under direct (racial) attack. Unlike typical occupation stress, racial battle fatigue is a response to the distressing mental/emotional conditions that result from facing racism daily (e.g. racial slights, recurrent indignities and irritations, unfair treatments [. . .] and potential threats or dangers under tough to violent and even life-threatening conditions).

William A. Smith (2004: 180)

She reached into her make-up bag. She was rubbish at applying make-up, though she was quite comfortable with the fact. She had once listened to an item on *Woman's Hour* where a make-up artist had said it should take about an hour to put on foundation. She had laughed to herself, wondering in which comfortable world the woman lived that permitted such indulgences. Her own routine, if you could call it that, took five minutes and mainly relied on deft fingers as opposed to an array of professional brushes. And yet, here she was today, studying images from the internet about how to apply the final touches to her face.

Make-up done, she stepped back and surveyed herself in

the mirror. 'Those muthafuckers,' she thought, 'they won't know what has hit them.' She felt a joyous and wicked sense of satisfaction soar through her, as she imagined the shocked faces of her white colleagues as she stood before them.

A presenter on the *Today* programme announced the time. She needed to leave.

She stooped to tie the laces on the tap shoes. They were patent white and had cost more than she'd expected but it was important to get the overall image right. White was good. It stood out.

Shoes tied, she reached for the skirt, taking care to hold either end of the ribbon in each hand so she could wrap it around her waist. The fruit dangling from the ribbon bounced, jostled and tangled themselves around each other despite her attempts to keep them separated.

She was calm. Years of being undermined, ignored and overlooked will do that to you. You're confused at first, that first time they wheel out some crap about you. Stunned even. She managed to disentangle the bananas and wrapped the skirt around her waist. She recalled how her short-term research contract at a below-standard university hadn't been renewed – no money they said – and yet, two weeks later while she still had a month's notice to work, they had advertised for a new research assistant to work on the same issues, in the same department. She had queried this and that was when the nightmare began as the university attempted both to get rid of her and to protect itself from the accusation that it was doing just that.

She studied herself in the mirror, taking in the overall look. She was satisfied with what she saw, but something was not quite right. She looked too . . . too neat, too put together despite the ludicrous blackness painted on to her face. She unplaited her hair and dragged her fingers roughly through it. Better. Tap, tapping across the wooden floor back into the bedroom, she picked up two huge gold hoop earrings, bought especially for the occasion. There!

She attracted a few stares on the way to work but, for the most part, Londoners did that very English thing of pretending not to see, being transfixed by words and images glowing on their phone screens.

As she disembarked at Stone Hill station and walked toward the Malcolm X building (the university had renamed all its buildings in an effort to demonstrate that it was embracing decolonization) she began to feel a little nervous.[1] It was a feeling that was immediately replaced by indignation and anger as she recalled her time not just at this university but at all of those she had worked at. She would be fine, she told herself. It would be fine.

As usual, the meeting kicked off at 2 p.m. with the Head of Department apologizing for the lack of communication about the restructure. All fifteen members of staff in the room nodded or looked at the HoD sympathetically. For all the challenges, they worked well as a department and had each other's backs. Well, up to a point. The terms of the restructure were being filtered down from senior management with no consultation process and no clear understanding of how to influence what was going on.

She shifted in her seat. Despite being made of sponge, the bananas were very uncomfortable to sit on, and besides, she didn't want to flatten them.

Agenda item 5 was about student reps, accompanied by a reminder about the type of comments to write on students' essays that they would find most helpful. There was some joking and teasing about no longer simply putting a series of exclamation marks next to incoherent sentences and resisting the urge to write 'WTF?' on work written by students who clearly had never had the benefit of a grammar class in their lives. She was no longer listening, only preparing herself for the next item.

'Item 6: promotions and new appointments,' the HoD announced. 'We have a number of congratulations to give today,' she said with a smile and looked around the table, one of her eyes twitching with confusion as it fell momentarily upon Femi's bizarre look.

The HoD began to read out names:

'Stephen Jones, congratulations on your appointment to Senior Lecturer.'[2]

There was applause. Stephen beamed, nodded and said thank you.

Femi waited.

'Elizabeth Montgomery, congratulations to you for being appointed Reader.'

More applause. Elizabeth pretended to look coy. Despite the applause, few in that room actually liked her. She was rude, abrupt and, the ultimate insult of academia, not at all 'collegial'.

Femi was next.

She unbuttoned her cardigan to reveal an all-in-one brown leotard with half coconut shells covering her breasts. Finally set free, the bananas tumbled with abandon around her waist. She let the cardigan drop to the floor.

'Femi Adeyemi, our congratulations to you for your appointment to Senior Lecturer.' Heads turned toward her and the same robotic smiles were paraded. This was her moment. Heart pounding, she leapt from her chair and jumped on to the table, scattering papers everywhere. The applause faded.

Smiles re-formed themselves into pained grimaces of discomfort and confusion and hands froze mid-clap.

Femi started to tap dance, wildly, recklessly, arms and bananas flying in all directions. One or two steps were real – based on distant memories of dance school – but it was mainly crazed improvisation, legs jumping around haphazardly. She opened her mouth to speak:

'Thanking yous kindly, Mistress. Thank yuh.'

Her colleagues were dumbfounded. Not even the white male professor, who had been assigned as her mentor when she joined the university as part of a BAME Leadership programme, found it in himself to say anything.[3]

Bananas jigged and bounced and Femi broke into an exaggerated smile. 'Thanking yuh. Thank yuh all. I is so very very grateful, affa all, I is jus' a po' ignorant negra.'

Elizabeth gasped, grabbed her half empty cup of coffee, and leapt back from the table. Others stood, or attempted to do so with confused legs, shocked, speechless and eyes transfixed on the spectacle before them. The Head of Department – usually superb at retaining a calm, sympathetic smile even in the most challenging of circumstances – was pinned to her seat.

One colleague – Malcolm, the Head of Research – snatched up his laptop and started to make his way hastily to the door.

Femi stopped dancing. 'STOP! Don't you dare!!!' she yelled, finger jabbing in his direction, her voice no longer imbued by a fake Southern slave accent.

Malcolm froze, looking at her in terror. Sheaves of paper slipped from his clammy palms.

She pulled out a creased note from the waist of her banana skirt, unfolded it and began to read, in a voice calmed by the iciness of rage and long-suffering:

Research shows that Black and minority ethnic academics are undermined, devalued and their experience called into question.[4] It shows they have to work harder than their white counterparts to succeed. Research also shows that they are more likely than their white counterparts to consider leaving UK higher education institutions to take up roles overseas.[5]

She stopped, looked up and surveyed the chaos around her. Wide eyes were locked upon her, shocked, scared and baffled by the horror of the wild woman before them: part Josephine Baker, part Black minstrel. She continued, her voice now shaking with indignation:

And my . . . my experiences here at the University of Ell . . . Ellington have been no different from that research.

Wiping away angry tears, she jumped down from the table, grabbed her belongings and, her shoes clicking on the worn lino, made her way to the door.

Part II: The Oracle

[*Setting: a theatre in the middle of London. The stage is dark. The auditorium is full and the audience entirely white, bar one Black man with his white girlfriend.*
A figure stands to stage left in the shadows of the curtains. It is dressed in a dark, draping robe that kisses the floor. A hood hangs loosely about its head. The figure speaks words into the silence.
They are slow, deep, clear and dance with the faintest undertones of mockery.]
You want to know what happened to Femi.

[*It is the voice of a woman. She laughs, her face barely discernible in the darkness.*]

I *know* you. You may deny it, but I know you.

[*She raises her voice.*]

You think she is mad!

You think she is ungrateful!

[*She leans toward the audience and whispers*] I know you.

I know what you see, how you think, what you do.

You want evidence.

You want to hear her story. You want to judge for yourself, by *your* standards, *your* norms.

[*The audience is silent. Eyes are transfixed on the Oracle, trying to make her out.*]

Ha! [*The chuckle is loud, mocking and heightened by sound effects that make it reverberate throughout the auditorium.*]

Okay. Okay, I will tell you.

[*Silence falls once more as the Oracle glides slowly across the stage. She is in no rush. She wants their eyes to remain on her. She wants them to wait expectantly. She stops before she reaches the other side and turns back toward the audience. The rest of the stage is still wreathed in darkness.*]

You see, ladies, gentlemen, Femi – our protagonist if you will – is smart. Oh, she isn't just smart, she understands the importance of hard work. She *knows* how to work hard.

She is not like you. She did not grow up thinking the world belonged to her. She did not see herself on magazine covers, running schools, businesses, determining what makes the news and how it is reported. She had no handouts, none of those intimate 'let's go for a coffee' to discuss that job – that job which was never formally advertised.

Hers was a different life.

[*The cloaked woman laughs, a cackling, derisory intrusion that makes some members of the audience shift uneasily in their seats, thrilled, nonetheless, to have secured tickets to this sold-out, highly acclaimed performance. Being an annual member of the English National Theatre Company had really paid off.*]

Femi has always worked hard, but you don't want to hear about that. No, no, let me tell you about her time at the University of Ellington.

[*The stage lights brighten as the Oracle completes her journey to stage right. She stops and turns slightly to the middle of the stage. A screen previously enveloped by the shadows now reveals a video of a young, fresh-faced Femi laughing gaily as she walks up to the doors of the elite university.*[6]]

You see, Femi was one of the chosen few.

She was groomed ... courted you might say. She was courted by the University of Ellington to be one of their research protégés.

[*Femi enters the building, the smile still accompanying her. The clip stops, with Femi's frozen wobbly gaze staring brightly back at the camera.*]

You see, the University of Ellington ran a prestigious programme called the Vice-Chancellor's Distinguished Fellows. I expect some of you may have heard of it. You look the sort. [*The Oracle sneers as she casts her eye across the auditorium.*]

Femi was chosen – specially chosen – to apply. Femi is not used to being chosen. Femi is used to having to fight for everything she has. Everything.

But this time, the Head of School [*the Oracle gestures toward the screen and, as if by magic, it changes to show an older brown-haired white man, dressed in an uninspiring grey suit set off by a protruding round stomach, the consequence of one too many after-work beers*] helped her.

In fact [*her voice rises several octaves, not dissimilar, some in the audience muse, to the booming gravitas of that actor who played Hamlet last season*], the draft of her application went back and forth several times. She tweaked it, revised it, edited it. She did what was asked of her, working late into the night after she got home from her contract research job with its pitiful pay.

And then [*the Oracle pauses*] came the interview. [*Each word is spat out with weighty precision, hinting, it seems, at some as yet unknown dark misfortune.*]

[*The clip resumes, this time showing Femi sat before an all-white interview panel talking and gesturing. The panel members are listening without expression. Some names are flashed on the screen: Karen McMillan, HR; Professor Mark Engelman, Director of Research. The names of the three other white people are not listed.*]

You see, that interview went badly for Femi.

Not because she hadn't prepared. Oh, she had prepared.

Why? Because something went wrong. [*She falls silent. The volume is turned up on the clip.*]

PROFESSOR ENGELMAN: I do not accept the premise of your research that all white people are racist.

FEMI: The research did not set out to say that white people are racist. Rather it was interested in whether the Black middle classes have the same tools or resources available to them as their white counterparts and if they get the same returns, if you will, from their social and cultural capital as the white middle classes. What we found was that race got in the way of their success.[7]

PROFESSOR ENGELMAN: So white people are racist!

FEMI: Well, we have to understand that white people hold a power that people of colour in the UK do not.

[*Femi looks to the other panel members to try to include them in the discussion, but they are motionless, staring at some unknown point beyond her head. Professor Engelman refuses to concede. The HR woman looks at Professor Engelman but says nothing. Her expression reveals nothing.*]

PROFESSOR ENGELMAN: If Black people are not doing well then surely they are responsible for that.

[*It is not a question. There is an undertone of bitterness and anger in his voice. Femi is uncertain how to respond. She is used to receiving pushback on her work. After all, race is a contentious subject, but this feels personal. She feels that she is engaged in a personal fight with the professor. And in an interview? She will try again and provide additional academic evidence. He is probably just testing her. This is a highly competitive position after all.*]

FEMI: Evidence from the Commission for Child Poverty and Social Mobility shows that white, privileged men [*she wonders, on reflection, if this was the best example to use*] are most likely to be leading the institutions that have the most influence on what happens in the UK . . .[8]

PROFESSOR ENGELMAN: Ahah! So now it is about white MEN!

FEMI: I am not singling out white men. I am speaking to the evidence. What I am saying is . . .

[*The atmosphere is awkward. Femi suddenly feels uncharacteristically nervous. Something is going wrong. She doesn't know how to retrieve it. Another panel member stirs from their reverie to move the conversation on. The screen freezes.*]

[*A hush falls once again upon the auditorium.*]
[*The Oracle glides silently to the middle of the stage. She stops abruptly and swivels to face the audience and is simultaneously illuminated by*]

the glare of a single, bright spotlight. She stands tall and surveys the audience slowly, her face fully visible for the first time.]

[*Her voice crescendos.*] You think this is about a *single* interview? A *single* moment in time?

You are fools! Fools, each and every one of you!

This has been Femi's life: spoken down to by line managers, shouted at by them, mocked even by a white female manager when she shared the horrors of period pain so severe that it had caused her to sign off sick from work. 'I don't believe in period pain,' the woman said. [*The Oracle seemed incensed.*] Oh yes, she really did. So much for feminism! So much for female solidarity! [*She nods emphatically as though to confirm the point.*]

Oh, I bet you're thinking this is just about Femi. Poor, little Femi. Femi needs saving. She needs fixing.

She's a one off perhaps?

Oh no! No, no, no. [*She leans forward and waves a disproving finger at the audience.*]

This. Has. Been. Her. Life.

And it was her parents' life. You think they came here to the UK to take on the shitty jobs you lot did not want? You think that's why they left their lives back home? You think Femi's mother *wanted* to explain to that idiot colleague – albeit with bemused undertones – that no, they don't live in trees?

This has been their life!

Femi's best friend Andrea? It has been *her* life.

And Andrea's brother? Oh, his life also.

[*She slows to a well-paced, considered narrative.*] Femi and Andrea used to have lunch together every other weekend. They would share stories about their week: about emotionally unavailable men and the tedium of dating, about some

29

new family crisis, but, more often than not, they would talk about the perils of trying to navigate the workplace and etch out some modicum of success in line with their overachieving dispositions. Andrea's challenge? She was tormented by an unsupportive, insecure line manager.

And they used to take it in turn, Femi and Andrea, to share their tales of woe. Sometimes, Femi consoled Andrea and sometimes Andrea consoled Femi. Sometimes . . . [*the Oracle appears thoughtful, wistful even, as though she too has her own tales that she could share*] there was no consoling to be done. They would just laugh, laugh and laugh again at the pain of it all. Laugh at the wickedness of you . . . of white people.

[*The Oracle pauses to allow the audience to digest the accusatory weight of her words. All are still in their defiance, in their awkwardness, all, that is, apart from the Black man who reaches into the darkness and takes hold of his girlfriend's hand so she might know that he does not think like that. It is all rather uncomfortable, but not as uncomfortable as the conversation they will have later that night on the tube on the way home. For until then neither had discussed race, at ease with the pretence that it did not matter.*]

[*The Oracle continues.*]

And Andrea's cousin Catherine? Well, she left her organization five years ago to set up her own business. Why? Why, you ask? Because she couldn't take it any more. Because she used to arrive home every evening a complete wreck.[9] Even her nine-year-old son asked her to leave.

[*The Oracle takes on a pathetic whimpering child's voice, hands drawn together in the pretence of pleading.*] 'Mummy, work makes you sad. Mummy, I don't want you to be sad. Mummy, I think your work is bad.'[*Her hands drop to her side and her voice resumes the slow solemnity evident in the opening scene.*]

Well, what is Mummy to do? Mummy has bills, Mummy has a mortgage to pay. Really, what is Mummy to do?

[*Pause.*]

Femi didn't get that role. She remained a lowly lecturer overlooked three times in her attempts to get promoted. The first time, they said she didn't have enough publications and so she wrote. The second time, they questioned whether she had brought in 'sufficient' funding, so she brought in more funding. The third time, they said that the overall quality for that year had been 'exceptionally high' so she didn't get through. 'Exceptionally high.' Oh, yes.

You think she imagined it was about race? No, my friends, this is not imagination. She watched as less qualified white men – and women – passed her by on the career ladder. She watched these colleagues with fewer publications, fewer grants, no public profile glide past her while she worked and worked like a dog.[10]

And many years later Femi – still at the University of Ellington and still a lecturer – was invited to a meeting arranged by the Director of Research (one Professor Engelman) aimed at understanding barriers to women's progression in the university. Femi suggested that they might also think about whether there were issues affecting white women that might be different for women of colour.

And what do you think happened?

Well, Professor Engelman went mad. Oh yes, ladies, gentlemen and non-binary friends. He went mad. He shouted at Femi, right there in front of thirty people, accusing her of always thinking about race.

[*The screen is lit to show Femi sitting at the front of a meeting room in a university with 25–30 white colleagues and Professor Engelman*

standing before them. The Director of HR is sitting next to him.
Professor Engelman's face is red, a pointed finger stabbing the air
that sits between him and Femi. He had shouted his accusation and
no one in the room stirred. All remained complicit in their silence.]
[*The screen darkens.*]

You see, there is no escaping race even if you want to try.

It would be another six years before Femi received her promotion to senior lecturer. By that point, she had suffered
what she thought was a heart attack and, stretched out on
the cream carpeted floor of her flat, she had muttered
prayers to a neglected higher being while trying to remember how to draw on yoga breathing in a pathetic attempt
to keep calm. In reality, it was a panic attack, the sympathetic GP told her. On hearing confirmation of her stress
from this neutral source, she broke down sobbing.[11] And
during those six years, she continued to hear yet further
stories of woe from colleagues at other universities in the
UK and in the US, and all while the University of Ellington was busy applying for a *Count Me In!* Diversity Award.

[*Upon uttering these last words, the stage lights click off. The audience*
waits with wide eyes and breath abated. Like seasoned lovers of clas-
sical music honed to recognize the momentary pause of the conductor's
baton, they know this is not the end and wonder what might happen
next. Then, to their delight, the lights slowly brighten, and a tall
lectern-like structure rises majestically from deep within the recesses of
the stage and towers above them. Though simple in design, the archi-
tectural finish is bold with jagged edges presenting deliberate dramatic
contrast to the clinical starkness of the set. The audience murmurs
with awe and curiosity then silence falls once more. A voice comes from
the top of the lectern.]

I know you will think that what you heard and saw this evening was just a story. [*It is not the Oracle. This voice is weaker somehow, though it still carries with it an air of defiance.*]

And in many ways, it does seem as though it is make-believe, but it is not. This is our story. Our experience. Our history.

It is true.

How do I know? [*The audience can't quite make out the owner of the voice no matter how they try to stretch and shift unobtrusively in their seats.*]

I know because it happened to me!

The stage lights swivel and swoop their full, powerful glare on the figure.

It is Femi. An older, greyer Femi but Femi nonetheless.

The audience gasps, stunned, struggling to take her in. It has all been true! The racism . . . right there in their so very tolerant country. How could it be so?

The Oracle steps purposefully from the shadows and raises her head toward the upper circle. With a single outstretched arm, she gestures toward Femi, who returns a solemn nod of acknowledgement.

The audience, still digesting the dramatic power of the performance, breaks out in wondrous, simultaneous applause and some in the stalls even stand in ovation.

What a truly remarkable play!

And they will speak about it on the way home. Some will draw comparisons with the latest novel by that British Nigerian author set in a north London estate which showed how gentrification impacted on the local African, Caribbean and Turkish communities. And some will deliberately find a way to make mention of the performance when in conversation with Black and Brown colleagues in order to show off that they *really* are thinking about this stuff quite seriously.

And the majority? Well, the majority will go back to their day jobs – their non-exec roles, their roles as directors in the private and public sectors, the jobs in the arts, in publishing, the law and the civil service – and not do a damn thing different.

——

This chapter draws attention to themes around workplace culture and progression within my own sector of academia. In many ways, as we will discover, the actual profession is almost irrelevant as patterns of racial inequality and workplace alienation are mirrored across sectors. Academia is interesting because, beyond coverage of students striking, housing and degrees, most people have little knowledge of what happens within the four walls of the university in terms of how it is managed and the experiences of professional and academic staff. The unevenness of the promotions process is reflected, in part, by an understanding amongst academics that it is easier to become a professor at a newer, post-1992 university (notably, former polytechnics) compared with the research-intensive Russell Group institutions. While there is a set of commonly agreed criteria required to be considered for professorship – these traditionally include a national and international profile, evidence of having shaped or impacted the field, strong research and teaching background, book manuscripts and publications in high-status journals – these are unevenly assessed within and between universities.[12] It is entirely possible for someone from outside the sector, who has never followed an academic trajectory, to be appointed professor despite not completely meeting the full criteria.

It was a combination of this information and the data regarding their low number that led to my carrying out research to explore the career experiences and strategies of UK Black female professors. I was interested in understanding why there were so few, how they described their time in academia and how they navigated higher education to achieve professorship. The below diagram depicts the typical career pathway for a Black female academic. It shows that disparities begin early in the career path as reflected by a series of setbacks such as not receiving constructive feedback on unsuccessful applications for promotion. The implications of this are obvious given that it limits the individual's ability to identify and address areas requiring development.

The diagram also shows how experience accrued in newer post-1992 institutions is not seen as equivalent by the Russell Group universities, meaning that Black female academics have to spend several more years proving their worth and credentials if they are to access or progress in those spaces. Even taking account of this, respondents in my study reported witnessing lesser qualified white colleagues pass them by on the career ladder and shared examples of racial microaggressions, of repeatedly being undermined and of not being supported by colleagues and line managers. It is the culmination of these experiences that serves as the backdrop for Femi's character.

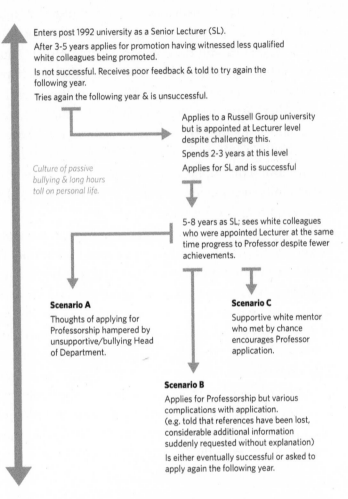

Enters post 1992 university as a Senior Lecturer (SL).

After 3-5 years applies for promotion having witnessed less qualified white colleagues being promoted.

Is not successful. Receives poor feedback & told to try again the following year.

Tries again the following year & is unsuccessful.

Culture of passive bullying & long hours toll on personal life.

Applies to a Russell Group university but is appointed at Lecturer level despite challenging this.

Spends 2-3 years at this level

Applies for SL and is successful

5-8 years as SL; sees white colleagues who were appointed Lecturer at the same time progress to Professor despite fewer achievements.

Scenario A

Thoughts of applying for Professorship hampered by unsupportive/bullying Head of Department.

Scenario C

Supportive white mentor who met by chance encourages Professor application.

Scenario B

Applies for Professorship but various complications with application. (e.g. told that references have been lost, considerable additional information suddenly requested without explanation)

Is either eventually successful or asked to apply again the following year.

Figure A: Typical career pathway for Black female professors[13]

2: The Meeting

... employers and employee representatives should [...] examine whether individual instances of racism contribute to the reproduction of racial inequality at a structural level, particularly in terms of disparities in levels of pay and bonuses, as well as discrimination in recruitment and inequalities in rates of promotion.

Ashe & Nazroo (2016: 26)

Jennifer glanced at her watch. Her next meeting was in twenty minutes, which gave her just enough time to finish writing the email she was mid-way through, gather the papers she needed, pop to the loo, reapply her lipstick and comb through her weave.[1]

She had worked at JBL (Jackson, Beckwith & Longley), one of the country's leading auditors, for almost ten years. When she had started, she was one of just four Black faces in her section of 186 staff.[2] One of these – Michelle – had left suddenly one day, apparently giving her line manager no notice and not responding to emails or phone calls which sought explanation of her whereabouts. Jonathan, with whom Jen had enjoyed many an intellectual debate over lunch, had left around eighteen months after Michelle, following a period of extended gardening leave and internal rumours of legal action. He had explained during the course of dinner several months later that, following a protracted battle between his lawyers and theirs, JBL had begrudgingly agreed to a payout and, as part of this, had forced him to sign a non-disclosure agreement (NDA). Jen would never forget that dinner, which they now jokingly referred to as 'The Surviving Babylon Dinner'.[3]

It had taken them three weeks to agree on a date for that dinner largely on account of the fact that the third person joining them from work – Sam – had struggled to find a babysitter. In the end, she decided that she would join them only for drinks and risk leaving her ten- and fourteen-year-old sons at home unattended for an hour. Any longer than that, she said, would be tempting fate and likely cause a row with her husband who was one of those traditional 'West Indians' who believed she should go straight home after work to continue her motherly and wifely duties.

The three of them had met at one of those slightly upmarket restaurant chains that the middle classes tended to frequent for Sunday brunch and their kids' birthday parties – not the one closest to work as that would have meant having to talk in hushed tones while looking cautiously over their shoulders – but a branch on the other side of the city that was not too far from the train station. Jonathan was even specific about where, in the restaurant, he wanted to sit (the furthest, darkest table away from the door, the till and the toilets), causing the bright smile of the otherwise perky millennial who was their waiter for the evening to fade momentarily as she left to ask her manager if such deviation from the evening's seating plans could be permitted.

Forty-five minutes later, after downing a large glass of Sauvignon Blanc, some olives and engaging in some innocuous office-related chit chat, Sam made her excuses and bade Jen and Jonathan goodnight. As the warm afterglow of their goodbyes faded, the two of them sat reflecting on the direction the evening's conversation might take next.

Jen thought about Sam. The last time they had managed to catch up properly, Jen had asked her again about applying for promotion to a director role. Sam was experienced, talented, well networked and respected, they were led to believe, across the firm. However, Sam shook her head and pursed her lips as she had so many times before when Jen had broached the topic: 'Why bother? I hear about the stress you go through. I just want to do my job, get paid, go home and be with my family. It's not as though they *really* care about listening to our concerns. Look how they treated Jonathan!'[4] There was little she could say to such a compelling rebuttal. Like Sam, Jen was aware that Jonathan had gone through a rough time at JBL but did not know the full details.

JEN: So, how are you?

JONATHAN: I won't lie to you Jen. It has been hell.

JEN: To be honest, I don't entirely know what happened. I know Robert went rogue on you.

Jonathan picked up his fork, pushed the food around on his plate and then laid it down again. He looked at her.

JONATHAN: These people! [*He shook his head.*] Yeah, Robert is an arsehole but the real source of the problem was the new CEO. He is a dirty piece of work. Robert and I used to get on well – I mean not hang out with each other's families or anything like that but . . . I took him to my club. I had his ear. He used to listen and act on the advice I gave him, including my take on clients.

And it was paying off. The size of that bonus I got last year? It was off the back of some very good intel I shared with him. It made him look good, the firm look good and the client was happy. I was making business. I was making good business for JBL, Jen.

JEN: I know. We all knew. [*She paused.*] So what happened?

Jonathan chuckled.

JONATHAN: The new CEO happened, that's what. Let me tell you, the moment that Justin Braithwaite started, Robert changed on me. He started interrogating my decisions, questioning my advice with a scrutiny that would put any seasoned micro-manager to shame. At the time, I couldn't fully understand what was going on, I mean me and this man had shared after-work drinks, broken bread together. I thought he and I . . . The tone of his emails changed . . . the tone and the length. Jen, this man's emails became like textbooks. They were long . . . officious! Whereas before, there had been a friendly, informal but nonetheless professional banter between us, suddenly they took on the kind of formality that you dish out to some incompetent, underperforming rookie. You know, like some shit HR would dish out.

Jen nodded. She knew of no Black person who liked HR. As far as they saw it, HR or whatever new-fangled name they'd given themselves, had one role and one role only and that was to protect the organization. They didn't give a damn about you as an individual – as a human being – and that was particularly the case if you were Black.[5]

JONATHAN: It was odd. It was suddenly as though I was speaking into a vacuum. Robert simply stopped listening to me. It was as if I had become his enemy . . . someone who couldn't be trusted. I warned them about Michael – about his behaviour, his refusal to follow my instruction as his team leader and they started gaslighting me.[6] Robert actually told me that Justin has a soft spot for Michael and that Justin thought he did that presentation last quarter superbly. Even when I copied them into emails showing how this man had pretty much fucked up a relationship with one of our major clients, you know what HR said? I told them what had happened, showed them the correspondence and asked for advice about how best to deal with it. You know what they said? That the email I showed them was a matter of – and I quote – 'subjective interpretation'. 'Subjective!' You know, I'm talking this through with my coach, with my friends and they are all alarmed . . . shocked and HR tell me that it is my 'subjective interpretation'. Jen, these people . . . they are something else.

He pushed his plate away, having only picked distractedly at a small corner of his steak.

JEN: You think Michael was their pet 'save the young Black man from the ghetto' project?[7]

JONATHAN: Who knows? The thing is, I'd been trying to support Michael. You know, show him how things were done. Anyway, I don't blame him – he couldn't see the bigger picture and the bigger picture is that damn Braithwaite who clearly has his own agenda. But Robert . . . Robert should have had my back, you know, pushed back. Instead, he hung me out to dry. The whole thing left me shaken to my core. Even Caroline was shocked by how much it affected me and, you know,

41

we've gone through some tough stuff together during the course of our marriage but this ... [*he tutted, shook his head and reached for his glass of Pinot Noir*] well, it's been tough.

JEN: Jonathan, I'm sorry. It makes no sense. You were THE rising star ... their rising Black star. I mean, you were doing all the right things: successful track record, popular, strategic, great networker, exceptional leadership skills.

JONATHAN: Well, we know how this goes, Jen. Never outshine the Master. Despite all of their 'we value diversity' shit, those same old rules apply. All I can say is, I hope that man sleeps with one eye open at night.

JEN: I hear you. You heard they've got some new recruitment campaign to attract more [*she assumes a tone of over-earnest sincerity*] 'BAME talent'.

JONATHAN: Yeah, I heard.

They were momentarily silent, each lost in thought about not just their own careers and the barriers and stress they had faced along the way, but about the accounts of Black friends, colleagues and even distant acquaintances 99 per cent of whom had gone through similar stress and setbacks. Jen sipped her wine thoughtfully.

JEN: We need a guide, some kind of handbook – you know, the kind of thing you get when you join an organization. We need something like that for us ... for Black people.

JONATHAN [*laughing*]: Yes! A 'surviving white organizations' guide! Surviving Babylon! I have an idea. [*He gestured to the waiter.*] What would be in that guide?

The waiter arrived and looked questioningly at him. She cast a polite but disinterested eye at his plate.

WAITER: Hi, how can I help you? Was your main not okay?
JONATHAN: No, it was great. [*He lied in the way that the English tend to when dissatisfied about their food but not wanting to cause a fuss.*] Could we have some napkins, please? Jen, have you got a pen?

And so they sat there, Jonathan and Jen, while the ebb and flow of conversation in the restaurant gradually waned, and together they scribbled ideas on the napkins the waiter had brought them about how to survive white organizations when Black:

Surviving Babylon

1 Always keep an eye on the job market. You can't afford to get too comfortable in your job and should always understand your worth beyond your current employer.
2 Develop a database of good employment lawyers. If they are your friends, even better, since it means you can have off-the-record chats if needed.
3 Save, save, save – always have 3–6 months of emergency money in case you need to leave your job sooner than expected.
They had debated this one for some time as Jen held the view that it was only bougie Blacks like them who were in the position to make such choices. Jonathan agreed but countered that all Black people needed to work to this as a fallback position even if it took them longer to get there. It should be something we teach our kids, he said.
4 Don't rely on your workplace to understand and appreciate your professional worth.
5 If you must attend work social events, do not stay for more than 30 mins.

6 Never drink at work social events for to do so is to risk vulnerability and lack of vigilance in the presence of whites. *This one had caused them such amusement imagining the wild scenarios and accusations that might unfold, were they to permit themselves such indulgences, that their waiter and remaining customers at a nearby table had turned to look toward them with consternation. Their list of potential charges from white colleagues was deliberately foolish, exaggerated and provocative: killing the manager's family dog; murdering Karen in HR's unborn child; cavorting with the CEO's precious Harvard-educated daughter. They both knew that you did not have the luxury of being anything other than fully alert and on full guard when in the presence of white colleagues even at social events.*

7 Never share personal information. You can guarantee it will be used against you in the future.

8 Related to no.7, on no condition display pictures of family members, partners or even the neighbour's cat on your desk or wall.

9 Learn to find a gracious way of saying 'that was precisely what I said' or 'actually that was my idea' at team meetings without a bitter or weary undertone because it is exactly the millionth time it has happened to you and it has rarely happened to any of your white colleagues.

10 Never leave your food unattended (also see no.7).

11 Always lock your office door (see nos.7 and 10).

12 Beware of the following white colleagues:
   a those with a Black or Asian partner, adopted child, mentee or 'best friend'
   b those with dyed hair (especially pink, green or blue) or nose rings
   c women (whether junior or senior to you)
   d men (especially if you are more senior than them)

    e those who have gone (either recently or in the past) to a country where they were in the 'minority' and subsequently use this as THE evidential basis of their understanding of racism

    f anyone with African art or sculpture

    g those proclaiming they have *a* (for it will usually be just one) very close Black friend who they talk about race with

    h your line manager

    i those who live in Brixton, Hackney or Tottenham and/ or refer to such areas as 'vibrant'

    j those who congratulate you a little too effusively in response to some minor achievement as if to suggest surprise and disbelief that you could do so well.

13 Don't wait for your line manager's approval or support; email senior leaders and tell them about your achievements.

14 Keep a folder marked 'Achievements' and dip into it when you're having a tough day, week, month . . .

15 Find a space (even if it's the toilet on the other side of the building or a broom cupboard) where you can breathe, detox, call friends on the phone and, if necessary, code-switch (women: take off your wig!) and curse the raas out of them.

16 Black women: unless you're prepared to stomach the conversation (about that 'beautiful material/turban/hat') and how you tied it (complete with a request for a live demonstration), don't ever wear a headwrap to work.

17 Don't get it twisted – dress down Friday doesn't mean *you* can rock up in your jeans and trainers like your white counterparts.[8]

18 If you still operate an office-based system, curse any man, beast or fowl who suggests that you would work better as a team in an open-plan office. Having sanctuary away from whiteness will help protect your sanity.

19 Switch off any music you might be playing before you reach your building or be prepared to lie about what you're listening to in order to avoid a tedious conversation about Black music.

20 Black women: don't be fooled into thinking that workplace gender initiatives for women have been designed with you in mind.

21 Whether you can convince your employer to pay for one or you need to do so yourself, get a coach and make sure it's someone who understands the dynamics of race and power.

22 No matter how well you (think you) get on with your line manager, don't go into appraisals or year-end reviews expecting your achievements to be properly acknowledged without some kind of bare-knuckle fight. Prepare case studies, collect data, look at trends and collate, date and order your file as though you're putting together a legal defence for a court case.

23 Always, always, always watch out for HR or whatever on-trend new name they have for themselves. They are not human (or humane) and their 'resources' are there only to protect the institution and at ANY cost. They will lie, twist, subvert, undermine and have you questioning your own damn mind. Do not say you have not been warned!

24 At the first whiff of anything that looks like it could be trouble, contact your lawyer. Don't wait for Sally or Karen from HR to get involved, for some line manager to suggest mediation or even to try to discuss matters in a mature, professional manner.[9] Contact your lawyer and start looking for your next damn job! Now!

Jen ran the comb through her hair and stared at herself in the mirror. She was thinking about the Surviving Babylon dinner she had with Jonathan a few weeks back. Trying to navigate your way to the top at JBL was hell. Several promotions and countless knockbacks later she had finally secured a role as a director and, apart from the Indian man they had brought in from the offices in Mumbai, she was the only person of colour working at this level. She sighed, picked up her papers and made her way to the boardroom for the meeting, marvelling at how well the organization managed its brand, conveying an image of cutting-edge business acumen alongside being the number one employer of a 'diverse workforce' – or so they said, and that's what the several awards and accolades also suggested. Just last week JBL had won a coveted *Count Me In!* Award for Diversity at the annual *Count Me In!* awards dinner held, this year, at the Dorchester on Park Lane. One of the partners – a white, gay man in a well-tailored dinner jacket and bow tie – had collected the award and commented explicitly on JBL's innovative work on gender and LGBTQ+ issues and (slight pause) the 'strides' they continued to make on race.

Jen remembered plastering on a smile and mechanically and painfully joining in the applause, though internally she remained unimpressed at what she knew to be the truth. Junior Black and minority ethnic colleagues constantly reached out to her asking for mentorship, advice and introductions to senior leaders. On more than one occasion, she had sat – tissue box at the ready – consoling young Black colleagues in a corner of her office as they stammered, through sobs or frustration, about how they felt unsupported by line managers or isolated in an environment predicated on the after-work drink. Or they complained about the casual conversations – initiated by white colleagues keen to show off their inclusive credentials – about the latest grime artist or cool spot to hang out in Hackney.

Jen sighed inwardly and, with a well-practised shake of the head, pushed these thoughts to the back of her mind as she walked into the boardroom where the meeting was due to take place.

A range of teas, coffee and artisan biscuits sat in uniform rows at a sleek table to the left of the door and notepads and pens, delicately embossed with the company's logo, lined each side of the boardroom table. It was not quite five to one, which meant that in this meeting-intensive culture she was early. She selected a seat carefully: facing the door so she could see who was coming in, away from the air conditioning and, most importantly of all, near the head of the table so that she was positioned within a clear line of vision and earshot of her manager. These were some of the tips that she had learnt from reading endless books about success strategies for women and people of colour in leadership positions.[10]

She sat down, preparing to take a final skim of the agenda, when Robert walked in. Robert was a tall, well-built handsome white man whose smiles and endless optimism never seemed to wane. 'Hello, Jen, how are you?' his French accent discernible even in these few words. 'Hello, Robert,' Jen replied, nodding back politely if not a little stiffly and returning her eyes swiftly to the papers on the table before her. She had learnt to avoid casual conversation with Robert not just because of what he had done to Jonathan but because of the way he constantly tried to attach himself to her in a bid to give legitimacy to his understanding of race. She recalled how at the section's Christmas lunch nine months earlier, he had made a beeline for her, squeezed himself into a seat between her and another Director, and proceeded to ask her which tribe she was from. The other Director, a white woman who headed up JBL's Equalities group, had squirmed uncomfortably and, blinking several times as if to dislodge the moment from her consciousness, turned to join in the conversation about dog walking taking place to her right. All the while, Robert's smile and eyes remained glued on Jen as he awaited a response which, in her initial shock, she had been unable to provide.

Try as she might, she couldn't avoid him.[11]

And then there was the Carlton project to which she had recently been assigned Project Lead by her manager. Robert had been allocated to her team but, unlike others, seemed to struggle with granting her the authority and respect the Project Lead position commanded. Though her instructions in team meetings were carefully calculated and precise and everyone else understood them, Robert frequently questioned her judgement and bombastically offered his opinion with little evidence to back up his retorts. And although it was not within his remit to do so, he assumed an air of authoritative condescension by writing emails to her that assumed leadership where he had none. She had lost track of the number of emails he had sent that began 'My view is . . .', 'We ought to . . .', 'Have you . . .?' for matters that were either none of his concern or were already being handled. Her attempts to politely but firmly remind him that it was her not him who was running the project were met with jovial agreement (though if one looked closely there was an icy determination in his eyes) and then promptly ignored in his next directive to her.

In short, Robert exhausted her.

And here he was once again, claiming a familiarity with race that he clearly did not have and with which she had no interest in engaging. 'I'm off to South Africa next month for a huge wedding,' he declared. 'You know South African weddings – huge. *You* know how it is; your family is from Africa.'

'We have had this conversation, Robert.' Jen's tone was deliberately slow and precise. 'My immediate family is from the Caribbean.' She made no effort to hide an exaggerated glance at her watch but Robert continued undeterred with enthusiasm plastered over his face and an overconfident glint in his pale grey eyes.

'Well, I guess it must be the same in the Caribbean,' he added and proceeded to share an account of how his children tell him that he really must be more circumspect when it comes to conversations about race, 'like the Germans,' he said.

Jen said nothing but was quietly seething inside, trying to work out how to shut Robert up once and for all. Another colleague (white, male) walked into the room. She looked up ready to say 'good afternoon' but, even though it was just the three of them, he ignored her and proceeded to engage Robert in discussion about a recent project he had been working on.

Jen had never understood this about English office culture – the way in which you could be involved in debate with colleagues one minute and the way they breezed past you the next, as though you were complete strangers. Any attempt to smile or nod in their direction was merely met with avoidance. She mulled over how, when she went back home to Jamaica, English people were quick to say hello – full, it seemed, of Caribbean sunshine and rum – while they barely acknowledged your existence once back in England. Still, at least Robert was now otherwise occupied.

The room began to fill. One or two people nodded in hello, others murmured amongst themselves, pouring coffee and crunching on biscuits, while waiting for the CEO Justin Braithwaite to arrive.

Jennifer skimmed the minutes of the previous meeting which she'd been unable to attend and there it was, item 6: Improving Workplace Diversity, and next to it, the name of the person who would be taking forward the agenda and assuming the new role of JBL's Race Champion: Robert Guillaume.

A heavy nausea swirled at the base of her stomach.

Section Equality & Diversity Lead was a role that would have been signed off by the Director of HR, the Director of Equalities and the CEO.

She got up from her seat and made her way toward the refreshments and, with a thousand pained thoughts swimming around her mind, poured herself a glass of water: the Christmas dinner; the endless derogatory comments; the complaints about Robert that she knew Jonathan had included in his grievance . . . Her hand shook as she took a gulp of the ice-cold mineral water. She looked across the city and drew in deeply through her nose and exhaled through her slightly open mouth in an attempt to restore some inner calm. And as she returned the bottle to its place and turned to retrace her steps to her seat Justin entered the room, took his position at the head of the table and called the meeting to a start.

———

My intention in this chapter has been to focus on how a workforce that is mainly white, and suffers from an under-representation of racially minoritized employees at senior levels, engages with issues of race. There are questions to be asked about how that organization makes sense of race and how this plays out in the form of cultural norms, assumptions and behaviours. This is particularly true for the leadership, as if they have a superficial understanding of inclusivity, this will play out in processes, policies and procedures, meaning that racially minoritized employees' experiences will be marked by insecurity irrespective of their individual achievements and track record. This is why efforts to improve the representation of racially minoritized staff must be accompanied by internal culture change.[12]

As such neither Jen's success nor Jonathan's departure and NDA can be viewed as unrelated individual acts.[13] Both come at a cost.

Our analysis of this chapter is not complete without considering Robert. I am interested in the behaviours he is able to get away with – particularly when compared with how Jonathan was treated – and what this says about who is and is not valued and protected by the institution. Robert's track record of undermining and harassing Black staff is ignored, or at least not seen as of sufficient importance, by senior leaders who made the decision to appoint him as Race Champion. Rather than regard this as a mere oversight or somehow irrelevant to our considerations, Robert's appointment – just like the use of NDAs – contributes to an understanding of the organization's culture and, despite their creation of the Race Champion role, reveals the senior leaders as significantly lacking in their understanding of race.

Interlude: How Many Times?[1]

It's important [. . .] to know who the real enemy is, and to know the function, the very serious function of racism, which is distraction. It keeps you from doing your work. It keeps you explaining over and over again, your reason for being. Somebody says you have no language and so you spend 20 years proving that you do. Somebody says your head isn't shaped properly so you have scientists working on the fact that it is. Somebody says that you have no art so you dredge that up. Somebody says that you have no kingdoms and so you dredge that up.

None of that is necessary.

There will always be one more thing.

Toni Morrison (1975, 35:46–36:42)

I am a Black woman.

I am a Black woman of Barbadian heritage whose parents came to the UK in the 1960s – my dad at the 'invitation' of the British government to work for London Transport, my mum a few years later to join him in marriage.

My parents prioritized education, repeating the mantra time and time again 'once you get your education, no one can take it away from you'.

And so, I was educated.

I am a Black woman who has worked hard – I worked hard at school, hard at university, hard at work.

I know many, many other Black women who have worked hard too and who, like me, continue to work hard.

And yet, I listen to them tell us that we lack aspiration.

I listen to them tell us that we fail because of the influence of 'street culture' or the lack of fathers or role models.[2]

I listen to them talk about women lacking confidence, about the need to network, the need to 'use your voice'.

But, as a Black woman, these things do not make sense to me. I already do these things, so I am left with questions.

I have questions that are to do with the very essence of my being – with being both Black and a woman.

I want to know:

How many times must we stomach conversations about our hair: 'How long does it take to style?' 'Can I touch it?'

How many times must we, as women of colour, listen to them talk about gender . . . the gender pay gap, gender and the boardroom, gender and leadership . . . and know that it never means us?[3]

How many times?

How many times must we think of strategies to avoid being spoken over at meetings – by white men and white women alike?[4]

How many times must we reread that work email which – despite the coded language – is a clear attack on our character?

How many times must we listen as white women espouse their feminist ideals while simultaneously and without flinching reject and subjugate ours?

How many times? How many times?

And as a young woman I read in order to answer questions that were just forming and those I was yet to ask.

I read bell hooks.

I read Fanon.

Zora Neale Hurston.

Maya Angelou.

I read Alex Haley's *The Autobiography of Malcolm X*.

Ralph Ellison's *Invisible Man*.

Frances Cress Welsing.

James Baldwin.

And they *fed* me. They helped me understand that I was not alone.

I read.

I read.

I read.

That reading continued when I became an academic – desperately looking for a language – for tools that would help me understand, negotiate and survive our experience.

I read but still questions remained.

I want to know: how many times must we pause to consider how to respond to white colleagues who think they are *down* with some aspect of Black culture? 'No, I haven't heard Stormzy's latest single' and 'No, it's not okay to ask me just because I'm Black.'

How many times must we watch as average white men – plumped full on privilege and the right connections – sweep past us to senior roles for which we are more than qualified but are rejected?[5]

How many times must we weigh up 'should I go to that Christmas party/after-work drink/work social and risk subjecting myself to some "friendly" comment about race that will sober my spirit?'

I have yet to work out how many times.

How many times must we leave work with the words of some cruel, undermining comment echoing around and around and around in our heads: did that really just happen? Did I miss something? Was it *me*?

How many times must we 'check in with ourselves' that we are not playing to the stereotype of the angry Black woman when we know that in fact there is so much to be angry about?

How much time does it take to learn that not all colleagues of colour are woke?

Please tell me: how many times?

How many times must I go home, switch off my phone and – my very soul exhausted – crawl into bed with a box set and ice cream . . .

. . . or read Maya Angelou's 'Still I Rise' for solace and affirmation?

How many times must I listen to Labi Siffre's 'Something Inside So Strong' to remind me that I *am* strong, I *can* do it, 'Yes we can!'?[6]

How many times must I tell myself that it is okay because my ancestors died for worse?

And what is the impact of all of this on our health, our friendships, our relationships?

How many times must we ask these questions?

Tell me, how many times?

How many times?

How many times?

3: Members Only

The white world, the only honorable one, barred me from all participation. A man was expected to behave like a man. I was expected to behave like a black man – or at least like a nigger. I shouted a greeting to the world and the world slashed away my joy. I was told to stay within bounds, to go back where I belonged.

Frantz Fanon (1967: 86)

A thick Dickensian fog had begun to descend on the streets of Mayfair as Miles made his way, guided by the map app on his iPhone, to The Afrókrema, one of the most established private members' clubs in London. Glancing up from the screen, he was momentarily distracted by a midnight blue velvet evening jacket in the window of a bespoke men's tailors. He paused to better take in the detail of the cut and the deep richness of the colour. 'Nice,' he thought, visualizing how well suited it would be for the next Black Leaders Awards dinner later that month. There was no price displayed, of course, which was natural for shops in this area. Still, that was entirely normal to Miles whose own suit that evening had been made to measure on Savile Row. He glanced at his watch. He'd better get a move on, given that he wasn't entirely sure where he was going. Turning, he crossed the road and made his way down a street lined with coffee shops, bistros, a health and wellness spa, a Michelin-starred restaurant and several independent boutiques.

Five minutes later, he came to a halt opposite a relatively unremarkable-looking building – for this part of town at least – and contemplated whether he should enter now and be twenty minutes early or wander around a while longer. Deciding on the first option, he crossed the one-way street and made his way up the stone stairs and through the doors of The Afrókrema.

Two rooms stretched expansively from the left-hand side of the hallway from where the murmur of men's voices punctuated the air, intermittently accompanied by hearty laughter and the comforting clunk of ice against heavy whisky glasses. Once upon a time, such sounds would have been accompanied by the dusky, masculine scent of cigar smoke. Still, the private veranda on the third floor with views that drank in the city provided space enough to accommodate such indulgences along with privacy for hushed conversations about politics, foreign trade and opportunities for business investment. The hallway floor was tiled and covered by worn but expensive-looking rugs, which led to a red-carpeted staircase whose end point was not apparent from where Miles stood. To his right, along a wide stretch of wall, was an imposing fireplace complete with a magnificent stone mantelpiece of a height that exceeded Miles's six-foot build. Paintings of stern-faced white men, gazing loftily into the distance or in apparent deep thought, abounded and, in the far corner, just next to the stairs, was a little wooden cabin-like structure where an elderly man (also white but less lofty in appearance) was busy studying a guest book with a pen poised delicately in his right hand. Miles approached him. 'I'm looking for the ES Society,' he offered.

The man glanced at him briefly, raised a disapproving bushy right eyebrow ever so slightly at the well-dressed mixed-race man waiting expectantly before him, and then gestured to the stairs: 'Second floor, sir, third door on the right.' This, the older man presumed, was what the future held now the club was trying to be more 'inclusive'. He returned to his examination of the guest book without so much as a second glance in Miles's direction. Miles noted the chill in the man's demeanour but said nothing as he turned and made his way toward the stairs.

The door of the room occupied by members of the ES Society was ajar and before he could step fully over the threshold, a balding, well-fed man approached him with hand outstretched in readiness to offer Miles a generous handshake. 'Miles, I am so pleased you made it. Here, let me introduce you. Miles, this is Casper Edwards, MD of Macmillan Enterprises. You'll have heard of them; they deal in construction. We call him Casp. George Brookfield, CEO of Hughes & White, the pharmaceutical company, and this troublesome bugger is Justin Braithwaite of JBL, one of the big four auditors.'

Chortles of indulgent laughter followed as Miles shook the men's hands and Justin leant in to whisper conspiratorially to him, at a volume that was clearly meant to be overheard: 'You have to forgive Ted. That's his way of trying to detract attention away from the fact that it is *he* who is the troublemaker.' The heartiness of the laughter that followed betrayed a history of friendship – probably at some private school in the country judging by the privileged tones that clipped their speech – that had clearly stood the test of time.

Aside from his host and the men he'd just met, there were five others, in deep conversation near the heavily curtained

sash windows. A further three stood near the fireplace (opu-
lent but not quite as much as the one on the ground floor)
nodding absent-mindedly to whatever it was the middle-aged
white woman in Jaeger attire was saying. Another six or so
older men were crowded near the table, helping themselves
to canapés. The men in the room were dressed in dark suits –
some were navy and others various shades of grey. The only
slight extravagance perhaps was in the ties and socks. These
varied, ever so slightly, in colour and style but, in line with the
strict, historic rules of the club, retained a sombre formality.

Miles's casual observations were broken by a timid 'Sir?' at
his shoulder. He turned to see a young man of East African
heritage – probably no more than twenty-five or twenty-six –
offering him a glass of wine from an ornate silver tray. He
selected a glass of red with a smile, a nod and a 'thank you'.
The young man returned a curt sober bow, took a step back-
wards away from Miles and proceeded to make his way with
practised precision around the room. Miles studied him, not-
ing how he always approached each person from the left-hand
side and nodded in unsmiling acknowledgement when a glass
was removed or returned to the tray. As for the men (and one
woman) in the room, they barely glanced in the young man's
direction. Arms were extended to engage with the tray but
their bodies remained turned toward the main focus of their
conversation. The young man was all but invisible.

'So who do we have here then?' Miles swallowed an internal
sigh and reached out to shake the hand of the gentleman who
had positioned himself before him.

'Miles Walker – very good to meet you. And you are?'

'Digbeth Winthorpe-Brown,' the man announced. 'I've
been a member here for over thirty years. My father was a
member and his father before him. Trying to encourage my

son to join – works in the City as a lawyer – but he is still thinking about it, whatever that means. What did you say you do for a living?'

Miles detested such shows of masculine pomposity, especially those weighed down by an unflinching privilege that the privileged refused to acknowledge or perhaps just didn't care about.

'I'm also a lawyer actually . . .'

'Oh?' Digbeth Winthorpe-Brown turned to face Miles full on and peered at him inquiringly. 'And where do you practise? Perhaps I've heard of it.' He smiled benignly.

'Perhaps you have,' Miles responded, growing irritated by Winthorpe-Brown's arrogant condescension, and then becoming irritated in turn that he was allowing this man to annoy him.

'I've just moved to Ashcroft & Boverty.' He had to think of a way to extract himself from this man's clutches.

'Ashcroft & Boverty? You mean on Fleet Street?' Digbeth's voice rose ever so slightly in surprise.

Miles decided to turn the conversation on its head – play with this ignorant git. 'Oh, so you know it?' He allowed the incredulity in his voice to match Digbeth's. 'Yes, Ashcroft & Boverty – ranked second in this year's Legal 500. You *must* have heard of it?'

Digbeth Winthorpe-Brown's nose twitched. The smile faded. He was clearly put out not just by the question but by Miles's sudden command of the conversation. However, an unhealthy concoction of a profoundly insecure childhood (mummy and daddy issues), an extremely privileged schooling (Eton followed by Oxford) and the comforts of wealth (generational) meant that humility and any degree of self-reflection were entirely out of the question.

61

'Well, of course I've heard of it. Yes, good law firm. Very good.'

He studied Miles.

'Well,' he mused eventually with the air of one used to being listened to and equally accustomed to paying little attention to the views of others, 'I can't say I have much time for those positive discrimination initiatives.[1] All this grouping people together –' he waved his hand dismissively '– because of what they look like. I was at some talk the other day and some young Bl . . . Bla . . . well, one of those activist types referred to me as white! Well, I can tell you, I gave her a pretty damn good piece of my mind. I told her: "*You* of all people should understand why I object to labelling people in such a way."'

He leant in toward Miles. '*You'll* understand what I mean, you seem like a pretty decent type of chap.'

'Actually, I'm not sure that I do understand. When you look at the statistics regarding—' Miles began.

'Anyway, look, must dash,' Digbeth interrupted, 'Dennis has arrived. We've been meaning to catch up for some time. Terribly good to meet you,' and off DW-B strode to the other side of the room.

Any mild pleasure Miles had experienced at hitting back with the name of his prestigious law firm had been short-lived. He cussed Winthorpe-Brown silently in his head: 'Pompous bloody idiot.' He was really fed up with such exchanges.

As he cast his eye in the direction in which Winthorpe-Brown had headed, wondering which of the two men he was speaking with might be Dennis, he noticed Ted (who had welcomed him earlier) moving with purpose to the front of the room. Attracting attention with a gentle tap of a knife against a wine glass, he began by formally welcoming those in attendance and reminding them not just of the history of the ES Society but of their ambitions for the future. Those ambitions included aims to increase the membership beyond the Society's 'traditional reach'.

At this point, Ted turned toward Miles and raised a glass. 'To our guest of honour and soon to be member – Miles Walker.' Cries of 'hear, hear' circled the air, glasses were raised and one or two were clinked together in toast but, as club custom dictated, there was no applause.

Fifteen minutes later, Ted had reached the end of his speech and Miles was in deep conversation with a relatively young-looking man about the prospect that the forthcoming general election would lead to the Governor of the Bank of England raising interest rates and the implications of this on the wider economy.

Glancing at the time, Miles realised that if he didn't leave within the next five minutes he would miss his connection to the last train. Giving his apologies, he exchanged business cards and the promises of lunch with the Eton-educated CEO and started to make his way toward Ted who, judging by the expression on his face, was clearly ensconced in a conversation of similar gravity.

En route, someone with whom he had not yet spoken and who was keen to welcome him to the Society stopped him to shake his hand and slap him heartily on the back. Miles was feeling damn good about himself and the evening. Maybe that Winthorpe-Jones (or was it Brown?) chap had simply been a one off. Turning to resume his path he was interrupted by the Jaeger-clad woman.

'You seem to have forgotten your tray. I don't suppose you could take this for me, could you?' she asked, stretching a neatly manicured hand to give him her empty wine glass.

A thousand thoughts, borne from weary familiarity with this racial code, collided messily in Miles's mind: *Seriously? You're confusing me with the damn help? No, she doesn't mean it. She's probably drunk. Yes, but I was introduced – to the entire room for fuck's sake – she knows who I am. And I'm dressed nothing like him. I look nothing like him. She is drunk. She must be drunk. Wait! Why the hell am I excusing this? Her? This isn't the first time this crap has happened. Okay, let's just get out of here and go home.*

The next morning, Miles stood wrapped in his dressing gown, carefully stirring porridge while it cooked on the hob in his kitchen. He was listening absent-mindedly to the *Today* programme. A new report had been published documenting the absence of 'BAME' people at the top of organizations and firms which have most influence on what happens in the UK. Law came off badly. His law firm was mentioned. The Managing Partner was being interviewed by one of the programme's long-standing journalists, Toby Halpin:

> *You are one of the largest law firms in the country. Are you seriously telling me that the findings of this report come as a surprise to you?*

The Managing Partner paused briefly before responding:

We at Ashcroft & Boverty welcome the findings of today's report. As you rightly say, Toby, we are one of the UK's largest law firms but our remit is global. We have offices in North America and EMEA. We are committed to meeting the needs of our client base and will take whatever steps are necessary to help us address that.

'Whatever steps are necessary' – but what are you actually going to do about it? Your firm has one of the worst track records in promoting and retaining ethnic minority employees. Surely that can't be something you're proud of?

As I say, we welcome today's report and look forward to working with ministers to discuss the findings.

Yes, but you've said that already. What I'm not hearing is what exactly you plan to do. Maybe we need to make the question more rudimentary: what do you see as the problem? Why are your ethnic minority employees falling by the wayside, if you'll forgive the turn of phrase?

Well, I simply do not agree with that analysis. I have answered you. The problem as I see it is that people from these backgrounds are often held back by a lack of confidence. They are not progressing because it's likely that they are not used to operating in these types of spaces. They do not have the skills – possibly due to educational background – to help them, but we at Ashcroft & Boverty are developing a new mentoring scheme that will help BAME trainees and those from disadvantaged backgrounds gain the confidence to help them navigate highly competitive environments like ours.

Miles recalled the night before.

He shook his head and switched off the radio.

Sitting down at the table, he began to eat his porridge. It was done just the way he liked it with one spoonful of honey and a sprinkling of chopped pecan nuts.

I have attempted in this chapter to draw attention to the ways in which race and class status work together. Specifically, I wanted to show how being middle class, the markers of which are often presented as the aspirational consequences of social mobility, offers only limited advantages for people of colour. There are two key elements to consider here. The first relates to Miles, his achievements and how he presents. The second pertains to the cultural norms of the private members' club and the expectations and judgements of its long-standing members.[2] As we have seen, the tension between these two states results in Miles being regarded as an outsider.

Like many membership-based clubs of this nature, The Afrókrema's elite class status is conveyed by its location and decor as well as through its history, rules and traditions. Though it may not be explicitly stated, these class-inflected ways of being also function as a filtering mechanism, siphoning off those who lack in financial standing and the appropriate social connections. As such, members are largely comprised of established white men and we receive confirmation, if needed, that this is a space for and of them evocatively depicted by the portraits that adorn the walls.

However, these markers and traditions are not merely a reflection of history but are maintained and given legitimacy via *existing* norms and the behaviours and communications of staff and long-standing members. That is, they embody the rules and culture of the club. This is evident in Miles's exchange with the porter, with the inimitable Digbeth Winthorpe-Brown and, of course, with the Jaeger-clad woman. I have intentionally presented these as brief interactions to highlight how those racialized as white signal dissatisfaction, disdain, a lack of acceptance of those who, in their minds, present as different from their perceived norm. Pierre Bourdieu's[3] analysis of taste and capital can be usefully invoked here to help explore this further.

Bourdieu describes taste – that is, 'manifested preferences' – as the 'practical affirmation of an inevitable difference'.[4] Therefore, The Afrókrema is manifesting in its history, its membership and customs a particular taste or preference for a certain order of things. However, Miles's presence, despite being authorized through an official statement asserting a (new) commitment to ethnic diversity, signals a disruption or break from that order. This must compel us to ask how those accustomed to the established ways might respond to the introduction of that which is new or different. I am suggesting that Miles's very presence – what he embodies and is seen to represent as a result of his skin colour – disrupts the institutional norms and the unspoken preferences of its established membership. Social mores, civility and even equalities legislation dictate that explicit or blunt expression of abhorrence (discrimination) is unacceptable. Of course, words, laws and dictates alone do not change behaviour, so we witness 'distaste' toward Miles being curtailed, managed, restrained in some form. This plays out differently depending on the status of the individual. The porter, though unimpressed by Miles's presence, does not actually verbalize his displeasure and gives Miles the help he has requested. His displeasure is evidenced through body language. Winthorpe-Brown initially seeks to exercise his distaste and judgement by seeking to undermine Miles. He makes negative assumptions about Miles's status and cultural capital and carefully juxtaposes this to a parade of his own status by signalling the longevity of his ties with the club. This is not a neutral first conversation upon meeting, but it is one where class and race lines are purposefully demarcated in the sand in order to convey power and hierarchy. Finally, the only woman in attendance exposes her disapproval of Miles's skin difference by rendering him irrelevant, invisible. Miles is not seen. His stature, attire and indeed public introduction to the entire group are not sufficient to grant him visibility or legitimacy within the woman's frame of reference. In this way, despite his middle-class accoutrements Miles becomes remade as just another Black body and indistinguishable from the waiter.[5]

Miles's exchange with Digbeth Winthorpe-Brown deserves closer scrutiny. We have already discussed the subject of social class as it pertains to their exchange. Let us now turn to race. Digbeth objects to being described as 'white' because, in his view, it means assigning labels to groups because of the colour of their skin. It means categorizing them and, in the process, imposing the idea of racial difference. However, this is a spurious argument which rests on a superficial interpretation of the actual dynamics of race since it implies that race only comes into being *when* such labels are used. Instead, and as we have explored previously, it is the meanings assigned to labels – and the subsequent treatment that this invokes – that sit at the core of racism.

There is a further point of note. By objecting to being called 'white' Digbeth Winthorpe-Brown is also seeking to retain and project an image of himself as an individual *without* a racial identity and, consequently, not part of a collective group who have in common a history, behaviours and attitudes toward racially minoritized groups.[6] This denial is both clever and highly strategic. By seeking to rid himself of a racialized identity, he becomes remade as a neutral bystander in the racial dynamic and, by default, not implicated in the rules, tensions and contradictions of racism. As such, his opinions cannot be said to be racist but merely the relatively objective expressions of an individual. Such concerted attempts at denial and the corresponding sleights of the hand are just some of the sophisticated ways in which racism and its counterparts of white privilege and power continue to be kept alive.[7]

4: 'Keep A-Knocking
But You Can't Come In'

The Executive Search Firm

Research Evidence: Hangartner, Kopp &
Siegenthaler (2021)

Recruiters using an online recruitment platform were
up to 19 per cent less likely to follow up with jobseekers from immigrant and ethnic minority backgrounds
than with equally qualified jobseekers from the majority population, according to research published in the
journal Nature.

Dr Dominik Hangartner, co-author of the paper
and Associate Professor in Political Science at the
London School of Economics and Political Science
(LSE), said: 'Our results demonstrate that recruiters
treat otherwise identical jobseekers who appear in the
same search list differently, depending on their immigrant or minority ethnic background. Unsurprisingly,
this has a real impact on who gets employed.'

The researchers found that there were only very
small differences in the time spent by recruiters on
the profiles of individuals from immigrant and
minority ethnic groups relative to those from the
majority population, showing that it is unlikely

that recruiters use ethnicity as a shortcut to screen out applicants.

However, at certain times of the day – just before lunch (11.00—11.59 a.m.) or towards the end of the work day (5.00—5.59 p.m.) – recruiters spent less time looking at all CVs. During these hours, when recruiters reviewed faster, immigrant and minority ethnic groups faced up to 20 per cent higher levels of discrimination.

Executive Search Firm: Rayner & Blue
Chief Executive: Duncan Jones
Head of Industry: Claire Allen
Personal Assistant to Chief Executive: Lucy Ainsworth

Company: Sinclair International
Director: David Sinclair
Head of HR: Becky Davidson

Candidate: Jasmine Williams

To: David Sinclair; Becky Davidson
From: Jasmine Williams
Date: Monday 25 June
Subject: Interaction with Rayner & Blue

Dear Mr Sinclair, Ms Davidson

Please forgive my contacting you out of the blue. My email concerns the executive search firm Rayner & Blue who are acting on behalf of Sinclair International regarding the position of Global Head of Diversity & Inclusion (ref. 37682).

I contacted Rayner & Blue on Tuesday 19 June to request further information about the role and application process. I was told that the consultant responsible for industry appointments – Claire Allen – was in meetings and would respond to my call the next day.

On the afternoon of the following day (Wednesday 20 June), I noticed that Ms Allen had looked at my LinkedIn profile on Tuesday, following my call; however, I had yet to hear from her. I called Rayner & Blue and once again asked to speak with her. When she came to the telephone, she did not allow me to introduce myself or explain why I was calling. Instead, she brusquely informed me that she was managing five appointments on behalf of Sinclair, stating: 'You cannot possibly imagine how busy I am and how much busier I would be if I took time out to speak with everyone who called wanting to discuss each of our advertised roles.'

Having spoken to employment agencies regarding advertised roles in the past, I was somewhat taken aback by Ms Allen's abruptness and unhelpfulness. Nonetheless, I attempted to explain calmly that her name and telephone number were on the job details and, indeed, there was a statement inviting interested parties to make contact if they wanted further information. Ms Allen conceded that this was the case but remarked that I had not even taken the time to send in my CV so, therefore, she had no idea with whom she was speaking. Of course, I knew this to be untrue and pointed out that she had looked at my LinkedIn profile on more than one occasion. I suggested that she may well have been able to answer my questions during the time she had taken to express her dissatisfaction with my having called her. At this point she fell silent and I took the opportunity, such as it was, to ask my questions, which she answered curtly and succinctly and without the detail and understanding that I had been after.

Perturbed by this but nonetheless determined to have my questions answered, I called the office again an hour later in the hope of speaking with Duncan Jones, the Managing Director of Rayner & Blue, whose name also appears on their website as someone prospective candidates might speak with. Unfortunately, it was Ms Allen who answered the phone. She informed me that Mr Jones was at their Glasgow office that day and hung up without saying goodbye and without offering to take my details or relay a message.

Having found the number myself following an online search, I called their Glasgow office and spoke with Mr Jones's personal assistant, Lucy, who told me that he was not in fact in Glasgow but at their London office where I explained I had just called. She gave me Mr Jones's email address and mobile number and I sent him a message that same afternoon and placed a follow-up call to his mobile the next day. At the time of writing, I still have not heard from him.

I am disappointed that I have been treated in this manner by Rayner & Blue and am concerned that others may have been too. The inappropriateness of their treatment of me is brought into sharp relief given that the role concerns matters of diversity, equality and inclusion. This, in turn, reflects poorly on Sinclair's statement on their own website that they are committed to providing a 'supportive and inclusive environment' for all employees. The executive search firm appointed by Sinclair International clearly does not adhere to those ideals, and the entire experience has left me with no faith that, were I to apply, they would treat my application fairly.

I would be grateful for your response with regard to the above matters and whether Rayner & Blue will continue to act for Sinclair International in managing the appointment process for this Global Head of Diversity & Inclusion role.

Yours sincerely

Jasmine Williams

From: Duncan Jones
To: Jasmine Williams
Date: Tuesday 26 June
Subject: Global Head of Diversity & Inclusion (ref. 37682)

Dear Ms Williams

Thank you for taking the time to contact me about the above role. We spoke briefly today but I understand that as you were between meetings you were unable to speak at length. However, I did establish that you have received an unacceptable level of service from us and for that I would like to apologize.

I am afraid that when you emailed on Wednesday, I was unaware of your negative exchange with Claire and forwarded your request for further information to her. I know she has not come back to you. I now recognize that, given the circumstances, my forwarding your email to her will not have been helpful.

I have spoken with Sinclair International about your complaint and if you would like to share further details of what took place, I will endeavour to listen to your concerns and look into the matter more closely. I offer my apologies once again.

Yours sincerely

Duncan Jones

From: Duncan Jones
To: Jasmine Williams
Date: Friday 29 June
Subject: Re: Global Head of Diversity & Inclusion (ref. 37682)

Dear Ms Williams

Thank you for forwarding further details about what occurred when you spoke with my colleague Claire Allen. As promised, I have looked further into the matter and write to provide you with an update.

However, I must begin by offering my sincere apologies once again for any offence caused when you spoke with Claire. I understand that this has led you to the view that were you to submit an application it would not be considered fairly. If you had registered your complaint directly to me at the time, I would have been able to intervene in a more timely fashion that hopefully would have reinstated your confidence in us as a firm and how we would have handled your application.

I understand that, at the time of your call, a candidate had just arrived at our London office to be interviewed by Claire. This may have contributed to her sounding abrupt. However, we pride ourselves on our client and candidate care and I have taken the step of speaking with Claire's line manager regarding her telephone etiquette and managing clients and candidates when under pressure. We plan to introduce one-to-one coaching for Claire and will continue to monitor the situation closely. I am also personally monitoring all candidates being interviewed by Claire to ensure that there are no further glitches in the system and so that I can intervene at an early stage if necessary.

I hope this gives you some assurance that we have taken your complaint seriously. If you are still interested in applying for the role, we would welcome an application from you.

Sincerely

Duncan Jones

From: Jasmine Williams
To: Duncan Jones
Date: Tuesday 3 July
Subject: Re: Global Head of Diversity & Inclusion
(ref. 37682)

Dear Mr Jones

Thank you for your email of Friday 29 June and for taking the time to look into my complaint. I note that you have sought to address my concerns directly but remain dissatisfied not just with the original incident but also with aspects of your response.

My first concern relates to Ms Allen herself who you describe as having been stressed on the day she took my call because she had a candidate waiting. It is difficult to accept this by way of explanation for her behaviour because she was hostile on each of the separate occasions I engaged with her. She was also obstructive, failing to provide either correct or helpful information when I called requesting to speak with you. Ms Allen was also rather fluid with the facts. Her statement that she did not know who she was speaking to was undermined by the fact that she had visited my LinkedIn profile (which includes my photograph) several times following my first contact with your office. At no stage has Ms Allen herself provided either explanation or apology for her behaviour. Given the string of events, it is difficult not to come to the conclusion that it was bias rather than stress alone that played a role in Ms Allen's behaviour toward me.

I acknowledge your insistence that, had I complained earlier on in proceedings and to you directly, this would have provided me with confidence that the process was being handled fairly. I am sure you recognize the inherent tension in issuing a complaint against a search firm when you rely on those same parties to treat you reasonably and fairly in their assessment for a role. While useful to supporting organizations in their search, executive recruitment firms also act as gatekeepers as this incident exemplifies. Being known as the person who submitted a complaint does not bode well in advance of submitting a job application, not least because of the challenges faced by persons who look like me during the job search process.

As such, despite initially being interested in the role, I have completely lost faith in Rayner & Blue and remain disappointed that I was compelled to work so hard to try to find out information that should have been readily shared with me as a matter of process. I will not be applying for the position of Global Head of Diversity & Inclusion at Sinclair International.

I thank you for your time in seeking to offer a considered response to my complaint.

Sincerely

Jasmine Williams

To: Jasmine Williams
From: Becky Davidson
Date: Friday 6 July
Subject: Re: Interaction with Rayner & Blue

Dear Ms Williams

Thank you for contacting Sinclair International about your recent experience with Rayner & Blue. I have now had the opportunity to follow up on your complaint. I have spoken with Mr Duncan Jones, Managing Director of Rayner & Blue, and I understand that he has now responded to you directly.

I am sorry that you had a negative experience in your exchange with Rayner & Blue and hope that it will not dissuade you from applying. I have been reassured that their processes are up to date and fair and that they will apply the highest standards of rigour to their handling of this particular post and to the others they are responsible for managing on behalf of Sinclair International.

Yours sincerely

Becky Davidson

The Interview

Caroline flicked her blonde hair (colour courtesy of the over-the-counter dye in 'Sunrise Caramel' from her local Asian hair shop that sold all the accoutrements a Black woman could ever desire for her curls) over her shoulder as she always did when she was feeling insecure, which was often. She was at the top of her game professionally and well known and respected by at least some of those working in her field and by many others too foolish to know better. She'd written – with the help of a ghost writer – two books about diversity, focusing, as was central to her brand, on the idea that Love, Listening and Learning (she'd trademarked the three Ls) solved all ills and could (subject to her eye-watering hourly rate which organizations desperate to be seen to be doing something . . . anything . . . agreed to pay) bring even the most disparate of ethnic groups together.

Caroline's agent loved Caroline. Being the right shade of mixed race made her easier to sell and it had really helped that she had decided three years ago to spend disproportionate amounts of money subjecting her naturally frizzy afro to the Brazilian hair straightening process on a monthly basis. She always looked immaculate, spending at least one third of her week and an equivalent portion of her income having some part of her body plucked, plumped or polished.

Caroline was a professional public speaker and opened high-profile events at exclusive venues and gave after-dinner talks at the dinner parties of the rich and famous. She was even known to do the odd keynote address when the mood took her. However, this was not often as it meant answering those tricky questions about how to implement meaningful change which, in reality, she had no clue how to answer. When she stepped down from the podium – always to rapturous applause – many (but not all) of the Black women in attendance, and a greater number of white ones, slid in quick sycophantic steps to introduce themselves, get her autograph and otherwise pray that they might be lucky enough to be brought into her inner circle. So bountiful was the obsequious dedication of her admirers that Caroline could tweet the most banal commentary about her life – which she often did – and the odd observation about diversity (usually poorly adapted and unattributed from something she'd happen to have read in a magazine) and thousands of likes and retweets would follow.

Tanya was not one of the women vying for Caroline's attention, even though they had gone to college together and knew each other relatively well in a professional capacity given that they both worked in the diversity and inclusion field.

Behind closed doors, Tanya described Caroline as 'Shaniqua come lately' to reflect the fact that Caroline lacked expertise – qualifications or otherwise – in the field with which she had in recent years become synonymous. In fact, when she was younger Caroline had dreamt of becoming a catwalk model and, several awkward castings and many failed years later, had redirected her now embittered attentions to the beauty industry with every intention of opening a high-end mobile business taking cosmetics direct to the customer. She had 'fallen into' diversity only because she had frequently found herself answering questions about race posed by her extensive network of white, well-meaning (so it was said), well-heeled Chelsea and Primrose Hill types amongst whom she tended to be the only person of colour. They, in turn, drank up her words greedily and showed their awed appreciation by nominating Caroline for every conceivable award, prize and gong known to mankind. And not one to miss or indeed contrive an opportunity for over-indulgent self-promotion, Caroline posted every award, prize and gong on every social media platform she was signed up to, which was all of them.

Tanya, by contrast, had worked like the proverbial dog, accepting crappy part-time jobs to fund her way through undergraduate and postgraduate study and had suffered more miserable line managers while working as a researcher early on in her career than any person should have to endure, before moving to the private sector to do what she did best, which was to analyse data and make hard-hitting recommendations to those genuinely committed to change in diversity and inclusion. Her beauty regime consisted of slapping some decent high-end moisturizer on her face, lathering her post-shower deep chocolate brown body in organic shea butter and a make-up routine that took two minutes when she was working and zero when she was not. She wore her neat sister locks in an updo and rocked a style of elegant attire that was on the socially acceptable side of characterful. Her commitment, warmth and authenticity meant that she had a network of supportive contacts upon whom she could call at any time and had earned a large following of which she was barely aware.

The dinner was taking place in the Picture Room downstairs at the Athenaeum. Tanya had been there several times before but would have preferred, given the long day she'd had, to head home and curl up on her sofa with a blanket to watch some mindless series on Netflix.

Caroline slid up to her with a gracious smile and, pulling her to one side, whispered: 'I heard you were offered an interview for the Director of Inclusion role at Bishopsforthgate. I didn't know that you were looking. It's a great position. Many congratulations. I'm on the interview panel, which is how I know.'

Her smile broadened but the rest of her face did not move. Tanya was unimpressed though polite enough to respond with civility.

'I hadn't been aware you were involved.'

'Oh yes, I've worked with them for a few years now. I was nominated for their Global Changemakers Award last year but . . . well, the reason I thought I'd mention it is because we obviously know each other quite well and it wouldn't be ethical if I were involved in your interview. I've decided that I am going to recuse myself and wanted to let you know.'

Caroline seemed uncharacteristically upbeat and friendly. Tanya eyed her askance.

'Really?'

'Oh gosh, of course, it would only be fair. I'll drop the Chair a line in the morning. I just wanted to talk it through with you first.'

Tanya returned a cautious smile. The idea that Caroline could be on the interview panel would have been enough to make her withdraw her application. Though their professional interests were the same, Caroline deliberately avoided referencing Tanya's work in public and in either of her books, failed (despite 'bigging up' the sisterhood on Twitter on an almost weekly basis) to ever congratulate Tanya for her achievements and, on more than one occasion, had all but shoved Tanya out of the way when Tanya was in conversation with a well-known celebrity whom Caroline had been intent on meeting.

Tanya would write to the Chair of the selection panel herself to explain the conflict of interest.

On the day of the Bishopsforthgate interview, Tanya arrived half an hour early so she could familiarize herself with her surroundings and do a mental walk through of the presentation that had been requested of all shortlisted candidates. She smiled at the secretary who made the requisite chit chat about the state of British weather as she escorted her to the waiting room, before disappearing back down the hallway to her office.

Tanya dumped her bag and coat on the nearest chair and began to pace slowly around the perimeter of the room, rehearsing key points of her presentation and offering practised responses to anticipated questions. Mid-way through trying to think of an additional example of a time when she had demonstrated influence (in case the three she had prepared were not enough), a thought crossed her mind. Even though she'd received confirmation from the Chair's executive assistant that they had received her email about Caroline, it might be a good idea, now that she was here in person, to just triple check for thoroughness.

Pulling the door to behind her, she made her way back to the assistant's office and mentioned the email about Caroline.

The assistant looked at her blankly.

'Caroline? You mean Caroline Ecclestone? Oh no, she is here. She's in the room with the rest of the panel.'

The Chair of the selection panel strode purposefully into the waiting room where Tanya was now pacing back and forth in front of the window.

'I understand there is a problem.'

'Good afternoon. I'm so sorry, your assistant thought I should speak with you. I'm afraid this is a little awkward. I sent an email prior to the interview, which was acknowledged, which explained that Caroline and I know each other rather well. We both agreed that she would recuse herself from the panel.'

'I see. Well, I'm afraid that interviews are well under way, and Ms Ecclestone is part of the process.'

'Yes, yes, of course, I do appreciate that. However, as I wrote in my email, given the nature of our relationship, there is a considerable conflict of interest.'

'It is not uncustomary that people will know each other given the field and the level of seniority. It happens. Ms Ecclestone has worked closely with us for some time and was agreed to be an external member of the interview panel several months ago. I can assure you that all candidates are treated equally and on merit.'

'Yes, I understand. However, I did receive confirmation of my email and that my request had been forwarded to you.

I believe Caroline may have also written to the panel herself. I would like the opportunity to be able to represent myself and be judged fairly during the interview. In my experience, in situations such as this, where there is a conflict, the person would recuse themselves.'

'That is not going to happen, I'm afraid. You have a choice: you can either be interviewed today for the Director position or you can go home.'

Tanya sat at the head of the table with the eight panel members spread before her in a horseshoe shape to her left and her right. Caroline was the first person to her immediate left. The Chair of the selection panel had resumed his seat at the top of the table furthest away from Tanya.

Caroline smiled at her sweetly.

The Chair opened proceedings by introducing everyone. Tanya breathed slowly and deeply in order to manage her annoyance, nodded in acknowledgement at each person as their name was said. She could not find it in herself to look directly at Caroline.

The Chair then explained the format for the interview: questions from the panel and then an opportunity for Tanya to ask her own if she had any. The presentation would be to a group of mid-level management colleagues afterwards in the next room.

The Chair then handed over to Caroline, who asked the first question on behalf of the group.

Tanya wrote down the question, not because she was nervous or even because she did not have a ready answer, but she needed to manage her rage and the indignity she had been subjected to. She forced herself to look Caroline in the eye as she answered and Caroline, in turn, looked back at her coolly and with a feigned air of innocence and curiosity.

The second question came from the Chair.

'As you know, Bishopsforthgate is the second largest employer in the UK. However, our data shows that we have some way to go to be truly representative in terms of BAME employees and Black employees in particular, especially at senior levels. Can you walk us through what steps you would put in place to help us really tackle this persistent inequality? How would you go about attracting more Black staff to our firm?'

Tanya looked at him in disbelief.

She looked slowly around the table at each of the people waiting expectantly for an answer and shook her head.

She looked back at the Chair. Then she pushed back her seat, picked up her belongings and strode purposefully from the room without uttering a word.

Research Evidence: Di Stasio & Heath (2019)

A field experiment we recently conducted shows that British employers discriminate against job applicants with an ethnic minority background when making hiring decisions. We applied to nearly 3200 jobs, randomly varying the minority background of fictitious job applicants while holding their skills, qualifications and work experience constant. On average, nearly one in four applicants from the majority group (24%) received a positive response (i.e. callback) from employers. The job search effort was less successful for ethnic minorities who, despite having identical resumes and cover letters, needed to send 60%

fairly once she is in the role. Therefore, just as the discriminatory behaviours of key personnel restricted the possibility of success for the main characters in this chapter, anonymous applications work in the same way. They merely mask the employer's biases and do not directly resolve them.[3]

more applications in order to receive as many callba[ck]
as the majority group. The discrimination encounte[d]
by minorities does not vary by gender.

——

This chapter has focused on the employment market an[d],
specifically, the ways in which the executive search fir[m]
and the interview process can restrict access to job opportunities even for suitably qualified candidates.[1] I have
been particularly concerned with the subtle ways in which
exclusion operates, given that the experiences of both
characters are not likely to be captured in conventional
data approaches to assessing the underrepresentation of
racially minoritized groups in the workplace.

Evidence that there are barriers at these early stages of
the employment pipeline is not new. Researchers have
employed a procedure known as 'correspondence testing'
in which, for example, the CVs of white candidates and
candidates with foreign-sounding names deliberately
designed to be the same are sent to prospective employers
in response to advertised posts. Findings consistently show
that candidates in the latter group are less likely to be called
for an interview compared with their white counterparts.[2]

A common response to this problem has been to
remove identifying material from job applications before
they are reviewed. However, this is not without its challenges since the removal of markers that might elicit bias
at this stage of the selection process might help, say, a
hypothetical Muslim woman secure an interview but does
not necessarily mean that she will subsequently be treated

Interlude: Committed to Equality & Diversity

We need to appoint someone for just a few hours per week to help with marketing and branding. Knowledge of social media would be a strong advantage.

Someone says that it should be a voluntary position. There are mumbles of agreement.

I am uncomfortable. I speak up. I say that this would be unfair and that the post should be paid. I say that we should not endorse the idea of people working for free.

My comment is ignored.

Someone – a white man – suggests that we might advertise the role amongst our networks.

I am stunned. I think I must have misheard and look around the table for expressions that might correspond with my disbelief, but others nod in response to what the man has said.

I object. I say that we know that social networks are classed and racialized. We don't simply want to share news of the vacancy amongst our mates. We should be thinking beyond our social networks, otherwise underrepresented groups will never get a look in.

One or two murmur in approval. The white man gives me a look that definitely is not friendly.

They discuss giving the role to an insider instead of advertising for it. They have someone in mind. That 'someone' already works in the organization. The 'someone' has a good track record, knows the organization well and has designed some important projects for us in the past.

That person is white, female and attended an elite university. Her existing role is full-time and has nothing to do with marketing or social media. Aside from knowing the organization (and them knowing her), I cannot work out how she is qualified for the position.

I look around the table in confusion. Is no one else bothered by this?

Everyone else nods. They are in agreement with each other, these people who look the same. The 'someone' would be a 'good fit', one person says. Another states: 'We can't correct the ills of society.'[1] That person does not look at me as they say this.

The eighteen men and women seated around the boardroom table are white. I am the only person of colour.

We are members of a Diversity & Inclusion Board for a major public sector organization.

5: The Christmas Party

The feeble British summer barely comes to an end before department stores, trendy gastropubs and supermarkets begin making plans for that dreaded time of year which has been commercialized beyond all spiritual recognition. Parents of primary school children who have been blessed with a creative hand as well as those prioritizing environmental concerns will attempt to make costumes for nativity-inspired school plays. And along with the painfully long family lunches, the thin, faded tinsel and the dispiriting but nonetheless obligatory Christmas songs on repeat, comes the annual event that every self-respecting Black employee fears: the work Christmas party.

Carol

This was pretty much how Carol felt about Christmas. Well, to be precise, she loved the warm cosiness of Christmas dinner, working out seating arrangements and planning which dishes to prepare, but that was in relation to Christmas *at home*. She did not like work events and particularly did not like the work Christmas party. They tended to be stifling affairs that encapsulated all the tensions and contradictions of the year past. In fact, she had long ago made the decision that life as an employee was not for her largely on account of having to deal with the disingenuousness and politicking of certain colleagues and having to constantly fight for recognition for her achievements. She had been appointed to three high-profile roles in the last ten years, two of which had ended in disaster. She had been headhunted for both and was initially welcomed with open arms. The Director of one – Goldstones Financial Ltd – had announced her appointment at the all-staff meeting with such enthusiasm that Carol had almost been moved to tears. She was copied into important emails, invited for endless cups of coffee and asked for her advice in a way that made her feel that her expertise was finally – some twenty-eight years into her career – being acknowledged and valued. Initially, senior colleagues listened with an open ear when she spoke and even the white woman she reported to seemed to respect her views as opposed to trying to belittle her experiences as she had come to recognize was customary for Black women.

Taking the role and their reactions seriously, Carol began to set out the ways in which the organization could effectively meet those parts of the strategic plan that fell within her remit. She was naturally proactive so, rather than simply wait for the next scheduled board meeting, she requested meetings with individual members to help secure advance buy-in for her proposal. That was when the ostensibly warm, collegial atmosphere started to change. Her line manager responded to her ideas with a distracted air and, aside from pointing out a missing full stop on the last page, neglected to provide any substantive comment. It hadn't occurred to Carol that she might have been doing anything wrong, that is until her appraisal when her line manager suggested, with a thin smile, that she might focus more closely on her annual objectives rather than 'working consistently beyond her remit'. Carol was confused and asked for specific examples so that she might reflect on where she might do better, but her line manager dismissed her concerns and told her that overall she was doing really well. She even put in place what she described as 'weekly catch-ups' with Carol, which, although she assured her were 'nothing formal', required Carol to turn up with a log of her plans for forthcoming weeks. Carol dutifully shared this information, always going beyond the basics of her role by showing initiative regarding existing and new projects. And her line manager always responded positively but again with little constructive feedback and direction.

It was only when she received an 'average' at her second annual appraisal – despite designing and leading on a series of high-profile internal interventions that the company had fallen over itself to celebrate on its intranet and monthly reports – that Carol began to suspect that her progression at Goldstones might be compromised. She expressed these concerns to her line manager, highlighting her experiences in the context of data she had obtained following a lengthy and quite tedious exchange with a particularly truculent member of HR, about how this might be potentially connected more generally with the underrepresentation of Black staff at senior levels of the company. Her line manager had cocked her head to one side and frowned in apparent earnest concentration as Carol spoke, and, when she finished, gifted Carol an understanding smile accompanied by the reassurance that senior Goldstones colleagues were already fully abreast of the types of issues she had raised. In fact, they were just about to recruit a 'BAME person' to their board.

That person turned out to be South Asian.

Her apprehensions increasing, Carol had spoken with her mentor (a senior white man who was a partner at a law firm) who advised her to do two things: speak to an employment lawyer and gather more information about the experiences of Black staff at the firm. Regarding the latter, she attempted to have a conversation with Derek, one of the two co-Chairs of the Black And Proud Affinity Network (BAPAN). She knew that her senior white counterparts viewed the group as an ineffective talking shop useful only to placate moaning Black staff. They had spoken about it quite casually in her presence as if she wasn't there and indeed as if she wasn't Black. As a result, she had attempted on several occasions to discreetly advise BAPAN's co-Chairs about formalizing the group and ensuring it had a direct line of communication with HR and the board. She had also suggested that they establish a quarterly meeting with the CEO so they could brief him directly on their activities and how they could be of support to the organization. That level of rigour would enable them to put together a case for funding to support the work they wanted to do. The co-Chairs had met her words with suspicion believing, mistakenly, that as the most senior Black woman in the organisation, she must be trying to use them to pursue some personal agenda.

As a result, Carol wasn't a huge fan of BAPAN and although she recognized that it was odd that someone with her seniority should confide to junior colleagues, she reasoned that it made sense given they had been at Goldstones longer than she had. She wouldn't give details but would speak in broad, hypothetical terms.

Only Derek had been available to meet her as his counterpart Angela was on annual leave. The meeting had been a waste of time as he had been preoccupied with only two matters: the fact that he had forgotten to wear a jacket that day in honour of their meeting (Goldstones took seniority and tradition seriously), and that it would have been better had they waited till Angela came back from leave. He wanted, he had explained, to make sure Black women had a voice. He was so preoccupied with this that he had completely overlooked the voice of the Black woman sitting before him. Had he been paying attention, he would have recognized the political significance of Carol contacting him to speak privately not just because of her seniority but also because she'd never done so previously. Indeed, when they met her opening words had been: 'This is a really sensitive matter and I'd like your assurance that we are speaking in confidence', which provided confirmation, had any been needed, of the gravity of the matters she wished to raise. However, Derek missed these blatant nuances and Carol had left the meeting feeling frustrated and more isolated than she had originally imagined herself to be.

She began to think about an exit strategy, carefully compiling a list of alternative organizations she might approach for an informal conversation about a new role, but was waylaid in her plotting by an urgent message from the Chief Executive (conveyed through her line manager) that a major client had expressed concern about the company's track record on race and wanted to know what specific actions they were putting in place to improve outcomes for their Black, Asian and minority ethnic employees and, in particular, those based in the UK. The Chief Executive and her line manager were now mobilized into a state of panic and wanted to know why Carol hadn't taken forward the very initiatives they had sidelined eight months earlier. Her line manager had said little when Carol pointed this out at her weekly catch-up meeting, although her emails started to take on an overly legalistic tone setting out in patronizingly granular detail instructions for Carol to take forward the most mundane of activities in a way that she had not experienced since her first casual job when she was sixteen years old.

As such, Carol had attended that year's work Christmas party only in the interests of appearance and due to her seniority. She would show her face and disappear as soon as she could. She planned to call a friend who was an employment lawyer that evening so she could check her understanding of the law surrounding constructive dismissal. At the party, she endured a conversation about the best places to travel for winter sun. Distracted by more pressing concerns, Carol had absent-mindedly proposed St Lucia, the land of her birth, and then had to stomach the colleague gushing about how very 'exotic' and 'vibrant' he and his wife had found it when they last visited and how so very friendly the locals were – 'such a friendly bunch – always smiling' – and did Carol have any thoughts about places where they might get some really 'authentic' food perhaps in someone's house and even better if the person lived in one of those old chattel homes. He wanted, he explained, to get a feel of what life was really like there beyond the high-end shops, big villas and the tourists. Carol had clock-watched like a teenager in a dead-end job and, once the obligatory thirty minutes had passed, grabbed her coat and bag and headed, at a pace, to the tube.

Chris

Unlike Carol, Chris loved Christmas. It was a time for fun and laughter with work colleagues old and new. You could always be sure that he would greet his colleagues' seasonal suggestions with openness and even throw in a generous handful of his own. And this year was no different. In a first in the history of the Civil Service, Secret Santa was to be theme-based and the theme was colour. The challenge, they mused excitedly for hours, was working out a colour they could all agree on. Picking an idea out of a hat was eventually deemed the most democratic method of selection and they had each groaned convivially when someone dipped their hand in and pulled out a piece of paper with the word 'yellow' scrawled on it. It sure would make Secret Santa challenging this year! There would also be a meal followed by karaoke that Chris was really looking forward to. And being an all-round good (and slightly naive) guy on matters of race, he didn't even flinch with discomfort when his teammate Tori (white, privately schooled in Surrey and now living in Brixton) suggested that they could play that 'Guess the Baby' game where everyone brought in a photograph of themselves from when they were no older than six months.

Chris was the only Black person in their department.

Little work was done on the actual day of the Christmas party. Chris donned a green elf hat with a little bell dangling at the end of it which tinkled every time he laughed (which was often) and his colleagues donned tinsel, reindeer antlers or Christmas jumpers and some all three in combination as the mood took them.

Dinner was fun. Chris got on well with his colleagues and responded openly when they asked him questions about his home life and his partner Carol, even offering to show them photos of her on his iPhone. By the time they moved to the karaoke room, they were all drunk including Chris who had consumed six G&Ts and half a pint of something he didn't even remember ordering. After much loud, disjointed discussion about whether they should break into teams and score each other on their singing, they had abandoned the idea altogether and simply took turns to stagger on to the stage with someone from their group selecting the singer's track.

Emma belted out an unfortunate rendition of George Michael's 'Last Christmas' and Giles sang, complete with highly finessed dance moves, Rick Astley's 'Never Gonna Give You Up'. It was Chris's turn. There was lots of laughter and shouting of song names which Chris was not sober enough to discern were mainly hip hop tunes with more than a splattering of expletives. In the end, laughing amenably, he agreed to perform Snoop Dogg's 'Drop It Like It's Hot'. He felt a little uncomfortable as he approached the stage, but through the spinning haze of his drunkenness he couldn't quite put his finger on why. His teammates laughed raucously and bellowed at him to 'be more like Snoop' and to 'do the moves' with Tori attempting to mirror Snoop's gang signs. Chris laughed and danced. Yet, he still couldn't work out why he felt increasingly uncomfortable until, that is, he approached the end of the first verse.

He made the very rapid decision that he would skip saying the word N**** and simply jump to the next one. His white teammates, however, fuelled by bounteous seasonal good spirit and the reckless confidence of having consumed too much alcohol, had different plans. They were all dancing now; the men were attempting to mirror some kind of faux Gangsta cool and the women, led by Phoebe the intern, were trying to out-twerk each other. Chris thought he noticed the guy who sat on the other side of the office (he could never remember his name) pretending to slap Tori's behind in time to the music as she tossed back her hair and laughed delightedly mid-twerk. As planned, he fell silent at *that* word but his colleagues belted it out at a volume so loud that even the party in the next room could hear.

Chris kept smiling and dancing, dancing and smiling but internally prayed that the song would come to a swift end. And when it finally did, he stepped down hastily from the stage and went to steal a Marlboro Light from Emma who apparently had given up smoking last month.

Standing outside on the pavement, with tourists milling around in slow gawping wonder at the lights that adorned the street and the menus on display in the restaurant windows, Chris reflected on his discomfort and his colleagues' use of the N-word. His reflections lasted all of thirty seconds before he came to the firm conclusion that he was being oversensitive and that it had all been in good humour. He took a final deep draw of the cigarette and blew the smoke through pursed lips into the cold air above his head, before throwing the butt in the gutter and heading back into the basement of the restaurant for more Christmas karaoke frivolity.

Carol, Chris and the Christmas Party

The book Carol had been reading slid to the floor with a gentle thud, jolting her awake. She looked around her, slightly dazed and confused as to why she was still wearing her dressing gown and why the light was still on. Then she remembered. She had been trying to stay awake till Chris got home.

She glanced at the clock that sat ticking dutifully next to the lamp on the bedside table. It was 2.48 a.m. A wave of concern surged through her. Chris was never late. Was he okay? She patted the duvet searching for her phone, which

99

she eventually found nestling between the pillows on Chris's side of the bed. No voice notes and no texts. She was alert now. Something must have happened. She climbed out of bed and tried his number. It went straight to voicemail. She started pacing the room, her heart pounding with worry and, as she dialled his number again, she heard a creak on the wooden stairs that led to their room.

'Chris?'

'Yeah, it's me. What are you doing up?'

He offered her a lopsided drunken grin and realized, as soon as it was delivered, that it was misplaced so sought to rapidly rearrange it into an expression of sombreness. She stared at him, relief and anger swirling simultaneously through her.

'Where the hell have you been? I was worried.'

'Worried? I told you I would be out late.'

'You said you'd be back by one. It's now three o'clock in the morning, Chris.'

Chris sighed and wobbled slightly as he made to take off his jumper.

'Look, Carol, let's not do this. I told you work was having their Christmas do tonight. Seriously, why the drama? Why the drama, huh?'

He offered another inane grin. Carol glared at him.

'"Let's not do this?" Chris, all you had to do was call! And are you seriously telling me you've been at your work Christmas do till three o'clock in the frigging morning?'

Chris, his mind befuddled by alcohol, considered this might be a trick question but answered anyway.

'Um . . . yes.'

'And you couldn't call or at least text? What the fuck were you doing, for goodness sake? Actually, don't answer that – I can smell the alcohol from here. You got drunk? At your *work* do?' She shook her head. 'You're mad.'

'Christ, Carol, let's not do this whole bloody race thing, okay? Yes, I went to my work Christmas dinner, and yes, I got drunk. Yes, I should have called. I didn't. I'm sorry. Now let's just go to bed, okay?'

Carol glowered at him through narrowed eyes as he continued to wrestle with his jumper.

'Actually,' she said quietly, 'it wasn't me who mentioned race, Chris, but since you have, what on earth were you doing drinking with those people? You know how much of a risk that is.'

Having finally extracted himself, Chris dropped the jumper on the floor and leant on the wall nearest him.

'Look, I don't view this stuff in the same way that you do, all right? You know that already. So what if I ate, drank and sang a few songs with them? So what? It's work and I happen to like my colleagues.'

'Sang? You *sang* with them?'

'Yes, karaoke . . . and danced.' He grinned stupidly at her.

Carol stared at him incredulously as if only now properly seeing the man she had been with for the last three years.

'You got drunk and sang karaoke with them? You would risk your dignity, reputation and possibly career by cavorting with these people after hours?'

'Oh, bloody hell, just listen to yourself, would you: "these people". You sound crazy. They're just people, Carol. People who happen to be white. Who cares, for heaven's sake!'

'Crazy? *I* sound crazy? You think it's the same rules for them and the same rules for us? You wait till something goes wrong and see who they blame, or they get rid of first. You don't get it with your cushy childhood in the backwaters of

Leicestershire with your white parents and your white life. You've been fooled into thinking we're one big happy Benetton advert but, mark my words, it doesn't work like that.'

It was Chris's turn to glare.

'You're really going to throw my upbringing in my face? Really, Carol?'

'I'm not throwing it in your face. I'm just saying that being farmed out at the age of two and having zero contact with Black people till your teens . . . Well, you have missed out on some crucial information about how to survive in this damn society as a Black person.'[1]

'For fuck's sake, not everything is about race. Not everything is about the big, bad, evil White Man. Some of us need to get off our arses, mix and make an effort rather than harping on about race all the time. I suppose you'll tell me next that the so-called White Man is to blame for why we don't do well at school and for knife crime amongst Black people?!'

They stared at one another, each seething with annoyance. It was Carol who finally spoke: 'I am actually stunned. You just don't get it. I said what I did out of concern. I can't do this now, but we should talk.'

'Talk? I don't see what there is to talk about. In fact, I've already discussed this at length with Douglas, thanks. We've had some great conversations. He gets it.'

'Douglas? Who the hell is Douglas?'

'Douglas Adebayo.'

'You mean the politician?! The one who hates his own people? Who thinks racism doesn't exist? The one they wheel out every time there is some crap they want to say about Black people and race. May the good Lord save us!'

Chris rolled his eyes and sighed.

'Honestly, Carol, you can be so damn superficial sometimes. Douglas is a good man. He is ambitious and successful.
In fact . . . well, in fact we've been talking about my joining
the party.'

Carol looked at him dumbfounded. Chris stared back with
defiance. A train rumbled somewhere in the distance.

Eventually Carol shook her head, strode over to the bed
and, having located her headscarf under one of the pillows,
tied it around her hair and climbed under the duvet.

———

Many years ago, I chaired a panel debate at a well-known
international City firm where the speakers – senior Black
professionals from a range of industries – shared tips and
strategies about their roles and how they had worked their
way to their position, to an audience of fresh-faced Black
men and women. During the Q&A, I took a question from
a young man who had recently joined the firm where the
event was being hosted: 'What should I do when my white
colleagues ask me to go for a drink and I don't want to go?'
He sounded pained, as though the matter had preoccupied
him for some time. 'Plus,' he added, 'I don't drink.' As I
directed the question to members of the panel, it occurred
to me that for many of us positioned in the margins, the
workplace is often shaped by such dilemmas. These questions matter in the context of debates about representation
and inclusion because, even though informal activities do
not relate explicitly to performance, they can impact on
perceptions of collegiality, fit and belonging and, consequently, the likelihood of employment success.[2]

Extracurricular activities such as talks, team-bonding
exercises, well-being classes and after-work drinks represent

an extension of the institution's culture. No matter how they are framed, they are not neutral spaces even though they seldom feature in organizational considerations about improving racial justice or diversity and inclusion more broadly. In this way, we can begin to understand the workplace as representing a site of constant negotiation for racially minoritized groups. It is for this reason that I have focused on the work Christmas party. I have also used this setting and Chris and Carol's differing responses to it as a way of drawing attention to the fluidity of Black identity. While a central aim of this book is to demonstrate the existence of a racial code and its role in helping racially minoritized (Black) groups navigate mainstream white spaces, I am also keen not to homogenize what we might, by way of shorthand, classify as 'the Black experience'.

Carol and Chris occupy distinct positions in relation to their racial awareness. For Chris, his Black identity only pertains to the pigmentation of his skin. It does not equate to a complex understanding of Black culture, of racism or of the strategies necessary for survival in a mainly white environment. This is why the baby photograph game does not act as a warning to him that he should be alert to the possibility of further indignities from his colleagues in the future. His reaction to their use of the N-word corresponds to what we have learnt about him so far: amenable and prone to downplaying or simply not seeing race. He minimizes his own feelings and concerns as oversensitive and excuses and dismisses the actions of his white colleagues as mere fun. In this way, his colleagues are not simply let off the hook but their worldview – that is, their sense of entitlement to make use of the word with little consideration of its likely impact on him as a Black man – remains intact and is elevated over his suppressed feelings.

By contrast, Carol tolerates her work Christmas party. Not only is her understanding and experience of race different from her partner's but she encounters a series of challenges while in her role which reinforce her outsider status. Therefore, she attends only as a symbolic gesture of goodwill and, unlike Chris, engages only superficially with her colleagues while there.

Whereas in Chapter 1, *Acts of a Lone Woman*, we concentrated on Femi's reaction to a long-overdue promotion, in this chapter we centre instead on the overarching career trajectory from point of entry to potential departure. The below pictogram, produced by a Canadian-based non-governmental organization aimed at improving the health and well-being of community organizations in Québec, usefully captures key milestones and characteristics of this journey.

The organization's power is evident at every stage of the so-called problem woman's career trajectory. Despite her appointment and the apparent celebration surrounding it, her efforts at intervention are perceived not as helpful to inclusion and organizational growth but as destabilizing the status quo. The institution does not really want and so resists change, or we might perceive that there is a limit to the extent of change it is willing to tolerate and the problem woman of colour has tested the extent of this limit. This tension is expressed not through open dialogue, reflection and negotiation but instead she becomes remade as a problem and a threat.[3]

Taken as a whole, the diagram speaks directly and evocatively to my arguments about the existence of a racial code.

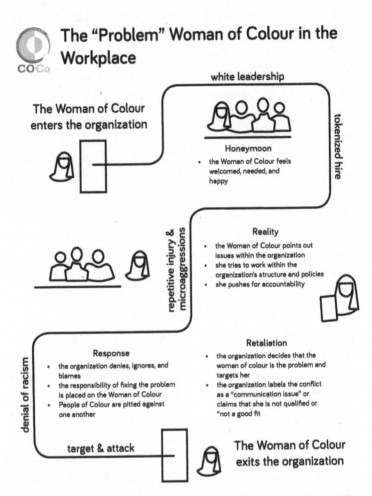

The "Problem" Woman of Colour in the Workplace

COCo

white leadership

The Woman of Colour enters the organization

Honeymoon
- the Woman of Colour feels welcomed, needed, and happy

tokenized hire

Reality
- the Woman of Colour points out issues within the organization
- she tries to work within the organization's structure and policies
- she pushes for accountability

repetitive injury & microaggressions

Response
- the organization denies, ignores, and blames
- the responsibility of fixing the problem is placed on the Woman of Colour
- People of Colour are pitted against one another

Retaliation
- the organization decides that the woman of colour is the problem and targets her
- the organization labels the conflict as a "communication issue" or claims that she is not qualified or "not a good fit

denial of racism

target & attack

The Woman of Colour exits the organization

Adapted from "The Chronicle of the Problem Woman of Color in a Non-Profit" by the Safehouse Progressive Alliance for Nonviolence
www.coco-net.org

Figure B: The 'problem' woman of colour in the workplace

White institutional norms and culture are to be maintained and protected irrespective of what the appointment might signify and even if it subsequently means creating discord and division amongst people of colour.[4] The organization's response exposes the lengths to which those in power will go to protect their power. And it shows people of colour to be at once agentic in their efforts to advocate for change and simultaneously overoptimistic – given that the organization *is able* to pit them against each other – in their assessment that the organization is willing to change.

6: V.O.Y.E.U.R.

As black feminists we are made constantly and painfully aware of how little effort white women have made to understand and combat their racism, which requires among other things that they have a more than superficial comprehension of race, color, and black history and culture. Eliminating racism in the white women's movement is by definition work for white women to do but we will continue to speak to and demand accountability on this issue.

The Combahee River Collective (1995: 239)[1]

In September 2018, I attended a reception at Downing Street to mark London Fashion Week. Although I had attended events there before, I had a number of preconceptions about what this particular one would be like. I envisaged the big names of the industry, the editors of high-end magazines and a healthy smattering of ridiculously tall and incredibly sleek-looking models. This was my moment, I decided, to wheel out the high heels and the awe-inspiring dress. In my head, I saw myself strolling elegantly (but decisively) up Downing Street and making various photoshoot-ready poses for the cameras outside Number 10 before turning on my heel and, with a graceful and mysterious smile, disappearing behind the famous black door.

As well as heels and a very non-academic-looking dress, I also decided to wear a headwrap that I would tie – my imagination told me – to a majestic height on my head; I would come out in full colour fashion fabulousness. But this was no casual decision for I deliberately and very consciously do not wear headwraps in spaces that are mainly white. This is because I know, and am not interested in engaging with, the type of scrutiny and questions that they tend to attract. Quite often this attention is presented as well-meaning curiosity but can carry with it an undercurrent of a fascination with the cultural practices of 'the other'. For example, I recall, in a moment of lapsed thinking, throwing one very quickly around my hair as I rushed to meet a friend at an event at her local community hall. A white woman who was also in attendance approached me and commented with an overly generous smile – while staring with awed bafflement at my head – how much she loved my 'turban' and how she had always been so very curious about how people managed to secure them on their head. My discomfort was not because she gave the item the wrong name or indeed that she did not know how they were tied, rather that her tone mirrored the same confused astonishment as when certain white people 'compliment' people of colour for basic or low level skills or accomplishments. Such observations are steeped in depths of disbelief as though such imaginings can only exist in the realm of science fiction. The woman's reaction was a racial microaggression. These are slight, persistent acts or comments that serve to remind people of colour that aspects of their cultural identity and practices and skin colour are judged to be inferior, odd or different when compared with the norms and experiences of white peers.[2]

Racial microaggressions place a quiet weight and stress on people of colour. They have to quickly appraise the situation – including whether they might have misread it – and if the microaggression is deemed to have taken place, a decision needs to be made about how to respond. Depending on their understanding of race and racism, one approach might be to reframe the situation so that it serves as an educational opportunity while, hopefully, also maintaining the patience and sanity of the person of colour.[3] Another option might be to smile (*read*: suffer) politely while attempting to change the subject, and a yet further tactic might involve engaging with the offence head on. Options which equate to mentioning race explicitly carry potential risk given that the white person may well become defensive. Attempts to ignore the insult may inadvertently be seen as granting permission to further conversation about race and cultural differences and, as such, invite even more problematic racial blunders and stereotyping. In the headwrap incident, this could easily, as had been the case countless times before, have progressed to conversation about 'ethnic' dress, trips to Africa or the Indian wedding attended last summer and the very fascinating customs and traditions witnessed there. Therefore, in making the decision, as I have, not to wear headwraps in mainly white spaces I am seeking to reduce the possibility of having to suffer such encounters. It is an act of deliberate self-protection.

This chapter explores the themes of offence and self-protection as it pertains to Black women's relationship with white women. As a postgraduate student, engaging for the first time with these issues in any serious way, I thought that equality for women of colour more broadly meant challenging forms of patriarchy and oppression enacted and upheld by white men and men of colour. I thought that there would be ample space in a collective imagining of feminism which would also fight all forms of racism. Yet, I witnessed white female academics who, while they defiantly laid claim to the feminism label, acted in ways that felt uncomfortable and alienating to me as a Black woman. At meetings, at conferences and seminars, I listened to radical white feminists boldly identify patterns of patriarchy and its impact on motherhood, sexuality and career progression while remaining silent about what it meant to be white.[4] I chose not to call myself a feminist (a term that still sits awkwardly for me today) for the actions of those white women showed me that I was not of them and nor were they of me. I continued to try to make sense of what feminism was and believed that it should include an analysis and challenge to patriarchy that was intersectional and obviously inclusive. It was only through an initial absorption in the work of the African-American feminist scholar bell hooks that I better understood the reason for my feelings of alienation:

> [. . .] from a black female perspective, if white women are denying the existence of black women, writing 'feminist' scholarship as if black women are not a part of the collective group of American women, or discriminating against black women, then it matters less that North America was colonized by white patriarchal men who institutionalized a racially imperialist social order than that white women who purport to be feminists support and actively perpetuate anti-black racism.
>
> hooks (1987: 123)[5]

As I progressed through my career, I met female scholars of colour who shared accounts – some personal, some based on research or on advocacy – which demonstrated how white women acted as barriers to our inclusion and to our success. I began to realize that our concerns were not based on personality differences between individual white women and women of colour but were systemic, that is they were grounded in historical ways in which white women occupied and enacted power in relation to us.[6] I was supported in my thinking by the work of Hazel Carby along with several other pivotal UK-based educationalists and activists, including Stella Dadzie, Ann Phoenix and Heidi Mirza who created spaces within and beyond academia which both permitted the complexity of Black feminism and drew attention to the ways in which mainstream forms of feminism were exclusionary.

I also observed that when challenged or invited to reflect on their actions and the arguments advanced by women of colour, those same proud white feminists responded with similar patterns of denial and defensiveness that not only served to keep the contours of whiteness intact but also resembled the avoidant behaviours they were urging men to confront. Sometimes their avoidance was characterized by particular essentialized forms of 'femininity and innocence' (Matias, 2020: 1) that served to perpetuate an image of purity and vulnerability.[7] This was conveyed powerfully by a woman I will call Helen, one of the respondents in a two-year research study into the educational experiences and strategies of Black middle-class families.[8] In the extract that follows, she describes an exchange she had with a white female friend who was married to a Black man. Helen takes issue with a comment her friend has made about Black men and a disagreement ensues:

> [. . .] she started to argue with me. I thought listen, you should be listening to me. You shouldn't be arguing with me because I am a friend, and I am trying to explain to you that

what you said was not appropriate and there are times when you just need to listen. [. . .] You need to be quiet and listen, and even if you don't agree with me now, when you think about it and mull over it and think 'well could I have said something different?' Instead, she started to argue with me because she knows everything about [. . .] [Black] men [. . .] So at that point I said okay I am going to go now because I had had enough. I had tried [to explain] and failed. [. . .] and then there were the tears [*laughs*] and that nearly finished me. Then came the tears: 'Oooh I'm so sorry, I'm not a racist . . .' And I just thought, here we go.

The subject of white women and how they deploy tears in moments of racial difficulty is one with which many women of colour are familiar.[9] In such contexts, tears work as a strategic device weaponized to detract attention away from the offending act and their taking responsibility for it. Tears can speak to both guilt and denial at having been caught out.[10] By crying or displaying upset, the white woman is remade as a damsel in distress who needs saving or reassurance, and the Black woman becomes positioned as the aggressor who has caused the distress and is therefore alienated. These tropes are common to each group of women. By accusing them of racism or of being racially naive, Black women undermine white women's investment in the idea that they are merely victims of oppression but are also perpetrators of it. This matters in a wider societal context where the white female is otherwise sacrosanct. Helen offered her own analysis of what happened with her friend:

[Tears mean the] [. . .] reversal of the situation. [. . .] 'You said something racist and made me feel bad but when you cry now you are the victim and what happened in that situation with the other mum in particular was I became the aggressor because I challenged you', and that is what the tears were about. The tears actually were strategic. You know the tears were strategic tears. They might not have been conscious strategic tears but they were sub-conscious strategic tears. [. . .] they do it a lot with racism. When you try and challenge it that makes you aggressive, and that is something that we have to deal with being called aggressive. Aggressive, chip on your shoulder but in this situation, it was turned around and I was made very much to look like the aggressive angry one because I challenged it. And I am left with that title now [. . .] because I spoke up.

As Phipps[11] confirms, this 'sanctioned victim status shields privileged white women from accountability in interpersonal interactions and in the political sphere'.

V.O.Y.E.U.R. is a satire in which these conventional racial dynamics between Black and white women are subverted and reimagined. Instead, we encounter a new reality where Black women are protected and able to live beyond the strictures of white female oppression.

Sandra paused outside the peeling wrought iron gate that stood between her and the large rambling, turn of the century house nestling behind trees and hedges some distance from the road. She was definitely at the right address: second building on the left as you walk up from the train station, the directions had said. It was dark. She fumbled around in her pocket, extracted her phone and held down the power switch as she'd been instructed: 'turn all devices off at the gate, not when you enter, before'. The gate felt cold to the touch as she nudged it open and made her way along the winding path to the steps that led to the front door.

The door was exactly as she'd imagined. It was large and wooden with imposing black bolts and an authoritative knocker at its centre. Sandra paused again wondering whether she really wanted to step into the world that stood beyond it. 'I am here,' she reasoned. 'Besides, things cannot go on as they are and it was an honour to receive such an exclusive invitation.' She took a deep breath and lifted the knocker, trying to remember the sequence: two knocks in quick succession, pause, three quick knocks, then a final loud one.

She waited.

She bit her lip, as she was prone to do when deep in thought, and assessed her surroundings. Aside from the gentle rustling of leaves in nearby trees and the odd hooting of an owl, all was quiet on this lane in the Surrey countryside.

The door opened silently, letting out a gush of warmth into the chilly spring night.

'Welcome, my Sister.' Sandra was greeted by a caramel-coloured Black woman whose natural dreadlocks curled elegantly to her mid-back. She was wearing a simple grey shift dress and matching boots and an adornment of silver jewellery which clinked in gentle rhythm with her walk. Her name was Candice. She led Sandra down a wooden floored hallway, past a set of stairs to a large open-plan reception room at the back of the house.

And in that room were Black women. There were Black women of all sizes, ages, heights and complexions. They sat or stood in small clusters deep in various conversations, some of which were sprinkled with laughter. Some gesticulated as they spoke, others listened attentively, nodding or shaking their head knowingly at key junctures. Others milled casually to and from the kitchen, which adjoined the room, with plates of food and drink. The atmosphere was electrifying. But what struck Sandra most of all was their hair. Some wore theirs in twist outs, others in Bantu knots, some hair was dyed sunset orange, others copper, warm chocolate hues, vibrant reds. There were women with sumptuous afros, long dreadlocks, short dreadlocks, dreadlocks which had been plaited while still damp and now spiralled across shoulders, on top of heads, down backs. Mixed-race women wore their hair in loosely defined curls framing their faces, or in tight unyielding piles scooped on top of their heads. There were women with closely shaved hair, patterns twisting left and right across their skulls. It was spectacular! Sandra had not seen such a rich cascade of beauty since the Natural Hair Show she had attended in Atlanta two years earlier. She smiled. It was the kind of smile that came from a powerful and somehow spiritual acknowledgement at seeing oneself so gracefully represented. Still smiling, she nodded at the women closest to her and they nodded back with the same knowing affirmation that they knew was foreign to untrained eyes.

Sandra turned back to her host. Seeing that she had finished taking in the room, Candice placed a gentle hand on Sandra's arm and guided her to a space on a sofa at the far end of the room. 'Come,' she said. 'It is time.'

The meeting was not as Sandra had expected. There were no minutes, no agenda and no individual introductions in the way that happened when she was at work. Presence was established by a single person calling out the names of those in the group in which they were sitting and those women, in turn, answering the call. There were forty-seven women in total. No one was absent. Sandra was the most recent woman to be accepted to the group having gone through a strict vetting process that involved answering a series of questions and providing video evidence about her experiences, activism and politics. In an odd procedure that had reminded her of a John Le Carré novel, she had to arrange to meet an unnamed individual in Waterloo Station at the height of rush hour in order to hand over her application. Email and postal applications were not permitted. That had been seven months ago but now, in the convivial warmth of the meeting, she was greeted with kind murmurs of 'Welcome, my Sister, welcome' and 'We are honoured' and several Namastes.

There seemed to be just one item for discussion: the pill.

At this point, Candice stepped aside from chairing the meeting to make way for a slightly older woman who was introduced to the group as Ms Wells. Ms Wells rose from her seat and slowly made her way to the front of the room, temporarily clasping the outstretched hands of some and nodding at others by way of acknowledgement and greeting. Ms Wells wore elegant navy ballerina pumps, a cerise-coloured dress with matching jacket and her black locks were tied up with an African-print yellow, cerise and blue cloth.

She reached the front and expectant eyes rested on her. She looked around the room with the casual ease of someone well accustomed to standing before large groups.

'Well, ladies,' she announced, 'we are ready.' She paused, allowing her words to sink in. Gasps of excitement swept the air. There were murmurs of indecipherable chatter as the women contemplated the implications of what they had heard.

Ms Wells raised a bejewelled hand and hush fell upon all present.

'Each one of you was chosen for your activism, your politics and the breadth of your networks,' she continued.

Her sharp dark brown eyes surveyed the room.

'You were also chosen for your scientific, medical and technological expertise. As you know, we have spent the last eight years testing and refining our product, a product that previous members of our group, who sadly are no longer with us, initially researched and developed. We have not only carried out tests to ensure its safety and reliability, but we have also created a plan to ensure that it reaches the furthest corners of this damn country and –' she paused, '– if need be, to our Sisters in the US and elsewhere in the Western world.'

'Yes', 'Of course' and 'uhhmmmms' swirled through the air.

'Initial trials proved highly satisfactory, but we wanted to refine the concentration in smaller sized pills to improve the ease of consumption. We have now done that.'

Ms Wells raised her voice to a crescendo. 'Tonight, ladies, we give each of you your pill!' She paused; clapping erupted across the room but Ms Wells raised her hand once again. '*I have already taken mine.*' The words were defiant and accompanied by a knowing smile and an affirmative nod of the head. 'Yes, that's what I said! I have already taken mine.' Cheers, squeals, laughter and giddy excitement swept across the women. One group – the ones Sandra had nodded to earlier – began to clap, others punched the air in a Black power salute, some embraced one another tightly and a few started to cry. The weight of the emotion was palpable.

'Yes, my beautiful Sisters,' Ms Wells continued, 'it is time.'

*

The train was less busy than usual despite being rush hour. Like most passengers, Sandra was lost in her mobile phone trying to respond to friends who had texted the night before. It was the only space she would have in a day filled with a speaking engagement and then back-to-back meetings.

'We will shortly be approaching London Victoria, where this train will terminate,' the automated female voice reminded commuters.

The journey always went too quickly, she thought. She checked her watch. Providing there were no delays on the underground, she would reach the British Institute for Esteemed Academics at least thirty minutes before her key-note address. This would give her time to meet her hosts and, importantly, get a feel for the room in which she was to present. Standing by the door, waiting for the train to pull into the platform, she smiled at the thought that she was the only scholar who was not yet a professor to make an address of this nature. Despite this, it provided some mild satisfaction for the years of hard work and relentless undermining by white colleagues she had endured. As the train neared the station her mind drifted back to her time at Kingsbury University and the way in which her line manager had consistently . . .

She was abruptly brought back to reality by a loud female voice over her left shoulder.

'Oh my God, your hair! It is a-maaazing! It's sooo beautiful.'

The voice belonged to a white woman, probably in her late thirties and dressed in an outfit that, judging by the cut and the colour, looked somewhere between Boden and Jigsaw. Her eyes were transfixed on Sandra's head. 'Oh my God, how long does it take to do?' The apparent intrigue at what she was witnessing had caused her voice to increase an octave.

Sandra felt the wearily familiar feeling of disgust and vexation fill her. Her soul and face hardened as she now whipped rapidly through her mental rolodex of responses for one that would be most apt for this moment. Of course, as was common in these situations, the white woman appeared to be oblivious to the cold steeliness of Sandra's gaze and instead was looking at her with a broad smile.

'I would *love* to get my hair like that,' she gushed. 'Is it heavy?'

Sandra's back catalogue was failing her; she couldn't find an answer quickly enough. She was looking for something between cool reserve and a touch of old school Brixton Yardie feistiness to put this damn woman in her place. She wondered how many moments like this she had experienced in the last few years and recalled the countless conversations she'd had with other Black women who had gone through the same.[12] And for one fleeting irrational moment, she pictured herself straddling this white woman as she lay on the floor and slapping her firmly and repeatedly about the face. And each slap would be matched in rhythm with a cuss about her temerity to intrude on her day, on her mood, on her identity, her very existence without so much as a second thought. The image gave her immense pleasure and as she pondered, lost in thought, the white woman continued to smile stupidly at Sandra, her eyes wide with astonishment as she drank in the apparent novelty of her hair.

And before Sandra could open her mouth to respond with spiritless words to the insult, the woman – in a move known and dreaded by countless Black women all over the Western world – lifted her hand and began to stretch fingers, dripping with colonial curiosity, toward her head. This white woman had just escalated the severity of the insult. Sandra's heart skipped a panicked and incensed beat. She attempted to step back but bumped into another passenger. So, instead she turned to face the woman full on ready to knock her hand firmly from its resolute path.

And then it happened.

The woman's hand reached about twenty centimetres from Sandra's head when she abruptly snatched it back and, with a feral wail that echoed throughout the carriage, collapsed writhing in agony on the floor. By this point, the train had come to a standstill just outside of Victoria, awaiting, the driver informed them, a free platform. Other passengers began to approach the train doors in anticipation of being the first to exit.

Sandra stepped back in shock. What the hell . . .? Perhaps she was having some sort of a fit. If that were the case, she should help her. She noticed the woman's bag which she'd dropped as she collapsed; some of its contents – lipstick, make-up brush, keys, travelcard, mobile phone – scattered haphazardly across the dirty carriage floor.

'Good God, what's going on? Is she okay?' asked an elderly white man looking dapper in a crisp, slightly creased sky blue linen suit. 'I . . . I . . . I think she's sick,' Sandra proffered. 'We should call an ambulance.' And as she raised her phone to call the emergency services, she discerned a series of red marks . . . letters slowly appearing across the screaming woman's forehead . . .

V

O

Y . . .

Still sobbing, whimpering and writhing around in agony, the woman pulled at her head frantically, making it difficult for Sandra to make out the remaining letters. The elderly man was trying to console her, pulling her hands away gently in the hope she wouldn't do herself damage.

E

U

R

Sandra's panic began to dissipate, replaced now with a feeling of quiet fear mixed with elation.

She slowly lowered her phone without dialling for help.

She understood.

The pill had worked. It had created a protective force field around her and so saved her from the white woman's hungry, racist grasp.

*

BBC REPORTER: Steve, you join us here outside Downing Street where the Prime Minister has called a meeting of the government's emergency committee COBRA to discuss the recent wave of attacks on women across the country.

STEVE: And what can you tell us, Sarah, about the nature of these attacks?

SARAH: The picture this evening remains unclear. What we do know is that at least fifteen women, aged between twenty-one and sixty-nine, have been assaulted in recent weeks, in what police are calling 'a series of unprovoked violent attacks' in a number of towns and cities across the country. The most serious of these was in Glasgow where a group of young women celebrating an engagement were attacked.

The screen switched to show a pre-recorded package. A group of white women, clearly out on a hen do judging by the now-dishevelled baby pink sashes with the words 'last night of freedom' splayed across them, were speaking over each other in a distressed state to an off-camera reporter. The bride-to-be spoke, her voice high-pitched and words tumbling over themselves from the shock:

> We were just out to have a good night like. I'm supposed to be getting married in a few days . . . I . . . we just went to this bar to get a few drinks. I don't understand. Look at us . . . [*the camera zoomed in for an up-close as she started sobbing*] look at our faces. My face is ruined. What am I going to do? These letters . . . what does it mean?

The clip ended and returned to Steve Johnson in the studio and Sarah Hennessey on location:

STEVE: And do we know anything about these women? Why, for example, they may have been targeted?

SARAH: Well, Steve, the police are still investigating but they have told us this evening that each woman reported feeling what they describe as 'an intensely painful electric shock' before discovering the word 'voyeur' branded on their foreheads.

STEVE: And do we have a sense of how the word got there or what it means?

SARAH: As I say, Steve, the police are still investigating what they describe as a 'puzzling and unique case'. What we do know is that these series of attacks across the UK are being treated very seriously by the government, which is why they are meeting today here at Downing Street. The Scottish First Minister is said to be monitoring the situation closely.

Sandra lowered the volume on her television as Steve asked Sarah whether 'the poor, defenceless victims' had anything in common. Aside from the women at the hen do in Glasgow, none, Sarah explained, is known to each other.

But Sandra knows.

She knows exactly what the women have in common, and for the first time in her life, she experiences a profound sense of relief at imagining the possibility of a future untethered from the constant surveillance and interrogation of her hair, her body, her skin through the lens of white women and white female beauty.

She exhales deeply.

As long as the pills continue to work, she thinks, 'I will be free.'

Interlude: Can I Be Your White Bitch?

'Oh. My. Gaaaawd! The guys must go craaazee when you're *really* dressed up!'

I lack sufficient expertise in American accents to identify where precisely the owner of this proclamation is from, but it is sufficiently loud, theatrical and camp to break my studied examination of the shelves in the dental section of a Midtown CVS pharmacy, where I'd been looking for a very specific brand of toothpaste for a girlfriend back home in the UK. I look up to my right to find the owner of the statement (compliment?) facing me. I give him a cursory but well-practised scan to assess age, clothing, class position and behaviour and possible signs that might suggest I am in danger. This information will inform how I decide to react.

The man appears to be well past middle age, is stocky, balding and white. He is, I estimate, no taller than me. I note his attire: his weighty round stomach is covered by an inoffensive thin cappuccino-coloured v-neck jumper and he is salivating at me in a way that compels me to start rapidly calculating how to seamlessly extract myself from the aisle and, if need be, the store with minimal hassle. Questions swim around my mind: is there something about the fact that this is New York and not the UK that should shape how I respond? Should I attempt to laugh off his comments as a mere joke while simultaneously sliding from the dental section to rush, at break-neck speed, from the store into the bright spring sunshine? I am still considering my options and potential exit strategy when he continues in the same overly confident drawl.

'I luuurve your nails – though you have one missing [noting my thumb nail which I'd slammed in a car door a few months earlier]. You're just *gorgeous*!'

'Thank you.' My words are clipped and accompanied by the sort of feigned, curt smile that I hope belies the haughty reserve of my Britishness: weighed down with courtesy but meant to deplete the conversation of oxygen. Believing, naively, that this has done the trick, I turn and resume my examination of the shelves for the elusive toothpaste.

'Seriously, I am the pervert your mother warned you about! Can I be your white bitch? I'd treat you well.'

I hear and digest the words but do not visibly react. 'My white bitch?' I cannot even fathom what this might mean. Surely, he couldn't mean . . .? Actually, I *don't* want to fathom what he might mean aside from the chilling realization that the fact of my brownness is clearly a turn on for this man, and I certainly don't want to contemplate whatever scenarios are cascading through his mind.

It is time to leave. Forget exit strategy, Nicola. Forget girlfriend. Forget toothpaste that is not available in the UK. Just leave.

But before I can move, he brushes past me, unperturbed by my repressiveness and lack of substantive response. He stands before the products on the shelves immediately next to the rows of toothpaste, rapidly scanning them from top to bottom. He picks up an organic diet supplement and asks my opinion about whether I think it will work for him. I have and offer no opinion for I am only preoccupied with wondering about my potential white bitch's likely reaction if I abruptly turn around and walk out on him. I start to edge, in what I hope is a casual, nonchalant manner, toward the beginning of the aisle – one eye on white bitch and one eye on the exit.

'Seriously, let me just ask,' he shouts after me. 'Can I have your number? I'd treat you well – spoil you, take you shopping, buy you shoes.'

I laugh. It is a laugh that is meant to display relaxed humour so as not to provoke him but internally I am concerned. I pick up my pace and disappear rapidly into the warm spring air.

7: Nigel's Story

National Centre for the Creative Arts
Press Release
17 October

The National Centre for the Creative Arts today has named **Nigel Small** its Director of Programming & Commissions. He will take up the post in January.

Small – the first Black, gay man to be appointed to a full-time, senior level appointment of this nature in the UK – joins NCCA following five award-winning years as CEO of Hackney Dance & Arts Theatre (HDAT) and as an acclaimed international playwright. Small is widely credited with having rejuvenated HDAT, turning it from a declining community outfit to a highly respected and financially sound cultural venue. HDAT has hosted some of the UK's best-known stars and been home to a series of sold-out performances before they went on to make their West End debut.

Small began his career as a performance artist in Tottenham, North London and went on to spend a year studying at the prestigious Debbie Allen School of International Performance in New York following the award of an Alvin Ailey scholarship.

As Director of Programming & Commissions, Small will help spearhead NCCA's new 'diversity of the future' agenda through a series of high-profile projects and commissions by scouting and recruiting talent and ideas globally. He will work closely with the Chief Executive Sally Cartwright.

Nigel Small said: *It is a real honour to be joining NCCA and to lead on this important part of its work. My sexuality and race should be irrelevant, but it must be acknowledged that I am the first Black gay man to take up such a position. Let's hope that I am the first of many underrepresented groups who gets to take up space – at all levels – in our arts and cultural institutions across the country. I'm very much looking forward to working with NCCA colleagues and to pushing the boundaries of how we think about and realize a truly radical and inclusive artistic vision.*

Sally Cartwright, Chief Executive of NCCA, said: *I'm delighted to welcome Nigel Small to NCCA in this newly created role as Director of Programming & Commissions. My ambition is to make sure we remain a world-leading cultural institution harnessing and showcasing talent through the Arts and through Culture to audiences across the UK and internationally. Nigel's arrival will help us do just that. For us it reflects our continued commitment to be cutting edge, daring and innovative and, crucially, to keep diversity at the top of NCCA's agenda.*

Tobias Hughes, Chair of NCCA, said: *Nigel stood head and shoulders above the other candidates. There was no doubt that he was the person for the job. We are thrilled to have him join us. He will really shake things up here at NCCA and that is to be welcomed.*

Notes to Editors

The National Centre for the Creative Arts was established in 1968 under the Commonwealth Integration Act to ensure that 'the experiences and interests of Britain's rich and vibrant past are reflected on our shores'.

For enquiries and further information:
Adam Gilchrist, Director of Communications
Tilly Wilkinson, Press Manager

From: Nigel Small
Date: Thursday 3 March, 16:32
To: Sally Cartwright
Subject: IMPORTANT: New exhibition – Slavery
Uncovered brief

Dear Sally

I understand the Slavery Uncovered brief will be sent to the board next week for approval. I'm writing this email to once again set out my concerns about the project and its likely impact on the Centre:

1. NCCA already has a reputation for poor treatment of its few Black and minority ethnic staff which, as you know, made international headlines last year.

2. NCCA has also received considerable negative press regarding its refusal to engage in dialogue about the various historical statues which adorn the façade of the building which were seen, back in the 1960s, as speaking to the legacy of the Empire and the emergence of the Commonwealth. It was only as a result of pressure from various campaign groups – and my involvement in liaising with them – that we were able to reach agreement about a plan to acknowledge the legacy of slavery with which they are associated.

3. To date, NCCA has refused to engage in debate about the various artefacts – many from West Africa – housed in its archives, many of which were acquired through dubious

means. As I mentioned to you in my three-year plan, our addressing this must be a priority.

4. Last month, despite my advice to the contrary, NCCA hosted a well-known white scholar – known for his views endorsing race science – as part of an event billed as 'Confronting Our Past'. Rather than offering a critical reflection of how to examine the problematic histories of some of our artefacts and the assumptions and beliefs perpetuated during past times, he endorsed the view that Black people are genetically intellectually inferior and debunked the existence of structural racism. And once again, despite my advice, NCCA issued a public statement not to challenge his views but instead to insist that we remain an unequivocal supporter of freedom of speech.

Sally, these acts undermine the Centre's proclaimed commitment to D&I, reveal it to be behind the times on racial justice and send the message to Black and minority ethnic staff – including me – and the community more broadly that we do not matter. Our efforts to improve the ethnic mix of our membership base (currently 98 per cent white and 87 per cent professional classes) will be further undermined. In short, the reputational risk in persisting with Slavery Uncovered is extremely great.

I recognize that email may not be the best medium to discuss this and suggest a meeting so I can set out some ideas about how we might together develop a programme that truly does unpack the complexities of slavery as well as help engage an audience beyond the reach of our current membership.

Regards

Nigel

From: Nigel Small
Date: Thursday 17 March, 10:13
To: Sally Cartwright
Subject: FWD: IMPORTANT: New exhibition – Slavery Uncovered brief

Dear Sally

Have you had a chance to consider my below email of 3 March? A conversation would be useful. It's important.

Nigel

From: Nigel Small
Date: Friday 25 March, 09:03
To: Alice Huntley
Subject: IMPORTANT – meeting with Sally

Morning Alice

I'm trying to get hold of Sally. I've sent her a number of emails over the last few weeks but haven't heard back. I'd like to schedule a 30min meeting with her next week. It's important.

Appreciated

Nigel

From: Alice Huntley
Date: Friday 25 March, 16:52
To: Nigel Small
Subject: Re IMPORTANT – meeting with Sally

Hello Nigel

I hope you are well.

Sally has received your emails but has been busy. She'll come back to you early next week.

Have a good weekend.

Kind regards

Alice

Alice Huntley

PA to Sally Cartwright

From: Nigel Small
Date: Friday 1 April, 08:03
To: Sally Cartwright
Cc: Alice Huntley
Subject: Important – Slavery Uncovered brief

Dear Sally

I have written a few times now and also left a message on your voicemail and with Alice.

I'd like to speak about the Slavery Uncovered brief. We will be shooting ourselves in the foot if we go ahead with it. The reputational risk to the Centre is too great.

Nigel

From: Sally Cartwright
Date: Wednesday 6 April, 17:59
To: Nigel Small
Cc: Alice Huntley
Subject: Re: Important – Slavery Uncovered brief

Dear Nigel

Thank you for your email.

My apologies for not coming back to you sooner. The budget on the China dance installation has needed my attention.

Yes, of course, let's arrange to speak.

Regards

Sally

From: Alice Huntley
Date: Thursday 7 April, 09:11
To: Nigel Small
Subject: Meeting with Sally

Dear Nigel

I'm following up Sally's email.

I'm afraid the earliest she can do is 2.30 p.m. on 18 April.

Kind regards

Alice

Event: Meeting with Nigel Small & Sally Cartwright
Location: Sally's office
Date: Monday 18 April, 2 p.m.

NIGEL: Thanks for meeting with me, Sally. I wrote at the start of last month and set out at some length my concerns about the new exhibition. You saw the email?

SALLY: Yes.

NIGEL: We simply can't go ahead with it in its current form. The plan for the soundscape, the foodhall pop-up with serving staff in so-called 'slave clothes', they're ... well, they're not appropriate.[1] They are offensive not to put too fine a point on it. And I know we still have a shortlist of potential speakers for the private view but a number of them are problematic to say the least. Sanctity Blue, for example, okay she's Black ... African American ... but she's viewed as highly contentious by many Black people. She basically describes anyone who admits to experiencing racism as displaying signs of a 'sniffling victimhood'. Sally, there are a number of high-profile, well-regarded Black *British* campaigners and academics we could invite instead – not to just give them a platform, but to show we are really engaged with the UK context.

SALLY: I see.

[*Silence.*]

NIGEL: There is a way that we can do this and do it well. I've set out some recommendations in a revised Slavery Uncovered brief. I've also worked out the budget – if we take my proposed route, it would bring us a great deal of positive press coverage AND save us money.

SALLY [*smiling*]: I take your point, Nigel. Leave it with me. I'll take a look.

NIGEL: Thanks, Sally. I am around this week and next and can make time to discuss this further.

From: Adam Gilchrist
Date: Monday 9 May, 11:13
To: Nigel Small
Subject: Package for new exhibition

Nigel

I'm following up Sally's brief about the new exhibition. Your thoughts on the below fonts and attached images would be appreciated.

FYI I prefer image 1 – the cotton-picking scene. We can cut away to a close-up of the man smiling, which would be a good alternative to the usual imagery we see about slavery. We don't want visitors to be put off.

Do you think some people might find the noose in image 2 distasteful? I'm less keen on this photo (Sally likes it) but we could pan out so that it is not the main feature of the shot.

SLAVERY UNCOVERED
THE EVERYDAY REALITIES OF LIFE AS A SLAVE

Slavery Uncovered
The everyday realities of life as a slave

Slavery Uncovered
The everyday realities of life as a slave

Did you have a chance to look through that list of invitees I sent you? There are a number of high-profile Black people we'd like to invite but don't have a direct route to

136

them. Do you know any of them? Could you facilitate
introductions?

Adam

From: Nigel Small
Date: Monday 9 May, 14:02
To: Adam Gilchrist
Subject: Re: Package for new exhibition

Hi Adam

Are you working to the right brief? These are the images
associated with the original brief. I set out an updated and
considerably revised proposal to Sally a couple of weeks ago.

Nigel

From: Adam Gilchrist
Date: Monday 9 May, 16:11
To: Nigel Small
Subject: Re: Re Package for new exhibition

Yes.

Adam

Event: Programme team meeting
Location: NCCA main meeting room
Date: 16 May, 14:00
Present: Adam Gilchrist (Dir. of Comms); Sally Cartwright (Chief Executive); Nigel Small (Dir. of Programmes & Commissioning); Abigail Lester (Senior Curator); Tilly Wilkinson (Press Manager)

SALLY: Right, agenda item 4 – the new exhibition. Well, I have some news! I am thrilled to announce that the board have approved our new exhibition Slavery Uncovered!

ADAM: That's great news.

TILLY: Yes, I'm really pleased.

SALLY: And there is more! I have approached Sir David Attenborough to provide the voiceover for the marketing video that will launch and accompany the exhibition. We are waiting to hear back from his people *but* he is said to be interested in having a conversation.

NIGEL: Sally, I wrote to you a few weeks back . . . we spoke. This is the original brief. I raised my concerns about this exhibition on a number of occasions . . . and to use David Attenborough as the voiceover . . . well, he is known for his work on animals, the habitat and the environment. It gives the impression . . . well, it risks further dehumanizing slavery and *reinforcing* the idea of Africans as chattel . . . as animals.

SALLY: What do you think, Adam?

ADAM: I think it is excellent news. Attenborough will add gravitas and authority to the exhibition – he is a well-known and much-loved voice. It will increase audience interest and participation. It's great, really excellent work, Sally.

SALLY: Good. We've also worked through a new activity for the installation.

NIGEL: And my point about Attenborough? About the exhibition? This is something we really must discuss. It—

SALLY: Let's pick this up separately, Nigel. I'd like to get through the agenda.

NIGEL: Sally, I did write . . . we spoke—

SALLY: Nigel, as I say, let's get through the agenda. I am aware of time. Let's speak after the meeting.

[*No one speaks. Nigel glares at Sally.*]

SALLY: Good. As I say, we've also worked through two new areas of content for the exhibition to really help get across just how terrible this slavery thing was. We want visitors to feel it . . . to really *feel* what it was like. The first is called 'Up Against the Clock' where people will first watch cotton being picked – we're working on identifying some old film footage, you know, some really great black and white grainy stuff – and then they will be invited to pick as much cotton as they can in a minute and then weigh it.[2] Obviously, it won't be real cotton [*she chuckles*]. We'll have to hire in some scales. Abigail, can you look into that – something large, industrial looking? They'll record the weight in a visitors' book helping to build the idea of competition and shared involvement in the activity. I think this will do an excellent job of bringing together people of different age groups, languages and nationalities – really ticking the box on diversity and inclusion.

[*Adam nods approvingly.*]

The second is called 'The Auction' where actors will perform the parts and audience members will be given individual score cards so that they can grade each of them on their physical attributes and potential suitability for plantation work.[3] We'll have to come up with a list of different types of plantation work to give to visitors to help them work out what the actors would be suitable for. I'm particularly pleased with this content: it means that we also will be publicly supporting Black actors, Nigel, which I know is something close to your heart.

[*She looks toward Nigel for a response. There is a heavy, awkward silence.*]

NIGEL [*his voice is quiet*]: Sally, this really isn't appropriate.

TILLY: The previous activity – the cotton one – is great but with this one I think we could be seen as glorifying slavery rather than thoughtfully educating people about just how awful it was.

SALLY: I don't agree. We're simply jazzing up the version they did at the museum in Liverpool. This is the first time in the UK that we will bear witness to an interactive slave auction – lots of audience participation. [*She pauses and then says thoughtfully*] We'll probably have to arrange a timed ticket entry system for this particular part of the installation. It's likely to be extremely popular.

ABIGAIL: I think we can make it work. We'll have to make some tweaks to it. Nigel, your oversight would be appreciated.

SALLY: Good, that's that then. Next agenda item.

After the meeting

NIGEL: Sally, a word?

SALLY [*her voice is sinuous, her smile thin*]: Nigel. How can I help you?

NIGEL: Sally, when we met last month, I gave you a new proposal for Slavery Uncovered. We're now going ahead with the original against my advice.

SALLY: Nigel, I read your brief. It was very . . . well . . . very interesting. Yes, really *very* interesting – but we need to really branch out on this one. We need to push the boundaries, encourage dialogue.

NIGEL: I agree, but using an exhibition to further undermine Black people is not the route to take. You brought me into this role to advise and oversee this agenda. My advice is that this is the wrong approach. Given NCCA's poor track record, we might have even started with a consultation process to run an initial idea by precisely the demographic that we are trying to engage. It's there in my brief.

SALLY: Well, I spoke at some length with Kojo about this. He agrees it's a good idea.

NIGEL: With all due respect, Sally, your seventeen-year-old mentee who has been in the UK for less than a year is not a consultation process and nor does he – as one young person – set the benchmark for what we do.

SALLY: I get that this means a lot to you, Nigel. I really do. As someone who has also experienced . . . well, who knows what it is to struggle and how challenging it can be to work your way up and feel as though you have to prove yourself, I get it. I do.

NIGEL: Sally, this is not about your working-class roots. This is about race . . . it's about how we, as a cultural institution, depict a brutal aspect of history with sensitivity and nuance. It—

SALLY: Okay, Nigel. Look, you are off to New York tomorrow and back next week, Thursday, is it? Why don't we call a team meeting to discuss both briefs and you can use the opportunity to set out your position to everyone.

[*Nigel pauses to consider the suggestion.*]

NIGEL: Well, I'm not entirely comfortable with that but I am prepared to at least start there.

Tilly's call to Nigel in New York
19 May

TILLY: Nigel, thanks for taking my call. I know you're busy over there.

NIGEL: No problem, Tilly. It sounded urgent.

TILLY: Yes, look, I don't want to keep you. Slavery Uncovered . . . the brief. I need your sign off, as the second signatory, on an amendment to the final budget.

NIGEL: An amendment? I don't understand.

TILLY: Well, Sally has decided on three more actors for 'The Auction' – two to join as slaves and the third . . . [*she clears her throat*] . . . um, she wants a third to keep their skin oiled. She said she saw it in *Roots* and wants it to be as authentic as possible.

NIGEL: For fuck's sake! You are kiddin' me?

TILLY: I know. I'm sorry. She did ask if any of the staff would take on the role but we thought she must have been joking. Basically, it means there's now an overspend on the budget, which is why—

NIGEL: This is just ridiculous. Absolutely bloody ridiculous. We may not even be going ahead with her version of the brief.

[*Tilly pauses.*]

TILLY: Why not? Has something happened?

NIGEL: We have a team meeting on Thursday when I'm back. I'll be walking you all through the revised version I did.

TILLY: Revised version?

[*Silence.*]

NIGEL: Yes. [*He pauses and then speaks slowly.*] The revised brief that Sally should have shared with you all on Monday.

TILLY: Nigel, I . . .

NIGEL: She hasn't shared it, has she?

TILLY: Er . . . no. Nigel, I . . . er . . . listen, you should probably know that she's fast-tracked the private view and go live date.

NIGEL: What?

TILLY: The private view – it's next week.

THE ARTS & CULTURE DIGEST

All you need to know about the museums,
heritage & cultural sector

Small leaves National Centre for the Creative Arts after less than six months

25 June

Jessica Longbridge

Arts correspondent

@jesslongbridge

Rumours of internal conflict rife as Small announces departure from high-profile role

Nigel Small has announced his departure as Director of Programming & Commissions of London's National Centre for the Creative Arts after just five months in the role. A source close to NCCA reported a series of 'ongoing challenges' between Small and the Centre's Chief Executive Sally Cartwright. It is thought that 'fundamental differences' over the much-publicized Slavery Uncovered exhibition brought matters between the pair to a head.

Slavery Uncovered was hailed as the Centre's ground-breaking creative endeavour showcasing challenging historical events through the use of new, immersive technologies. It opened last month to a lukewarm reception from critics and vitriol on social media by outraged racial justice campaigners and activists. Controversially, advertisements for the exhibition featured a smiling Black man picking cotton while another hung by a noose in the background. These were later removed following complaints from members of the public. In response to news of the exhibition, the well-known author and campaigner Justin Campbell tweeted:

> Slavery Uncovered? More like Colonialism ReDiscovered! It's like that scene in *Django Unchained* where Leonardo DiCaprio's character watches two slaves wrestling for his enjoyment. This is not innovative. It's the same old tired rubbish: @NCCA's new exhibition parades slavery for modern day white titillation.
>
> #sellout #racism #DjangoRechained

Small joined NCCA in January this year following a highly successful run as CEO of Hackney Dance & Arts Theatre. His role as Director of Programming & Commissions at NCCA made him the most senior gay Black man to occupy such a role across the entire museums and cultural heritage sector in the UK. Commenting on his departure in a statement released by NCCA, Small said that he planned to 'pursue other creative avenues in the months to follow'.

Sally Cartwright, NCCA's Chief Executive, said, 'We can confirm that Nigel is leaving NCCA to pursue alternative career options. We have enjoyed working with Nigel during his short tenure at NCCA and have learnt much about how to push the boundaries of diversity in a creative and considered way. We wish him the best for his future endeavours.'

The news comes as the latest Diversity in the Cultural Heritage Sector report shows declining numbers of Black and minority ethnic permanent staff at the higher echelons of museums and cultural institutions despite a number of initiatives to encourage their recruitment.

One Year Later

Small is headhunted by the prestigious American playhouse Spotlight known for forging the careers of high-profile African American stars including James Earl Jones, Diahann Carroll and Sammy Davis Jr. He moves to the US and takes up this appointment for an undisclosed sum.[4]

Eight Years Later

Sally Cartwright is appointed by the government to lead an independent review into diversity in the cultural industries. News of her appointment is met with widespread criticism, but the government remains defiant, describing her as 'a leading cultural commentator and supporter of the arts'.

Only the most tenacious of observers discern that her stepson by her first marriage is the Culture Minister.

—

The workplace serves once again as the setting through which to examine the subject of racial inclusion and exclusion. In this chapter, we consider the appointment of a high-profile Black person to a senior role and their experiences in their initial months. Given the scarcity of individuals in such positions, such appointments cannot be viewed as a neutral act for, as with Carol in *The Christmas Party*, they become a means of declaring, through carefully scripted internal communications and press releases, institutional commitment to diversity and inclusion and to particular strategic ambitions. The racialized identity – the very skin – of the appointee itself becomes a commodity to be paraded and capitalized on. The person becomes more than their experience and qualifications and is remade into a PR opportunity to benefit the institution's self-image and declarations of inclusivity. It might be the case that such an appointment really does represent the visible demonstration of the institution's sincerity and willingness to change. However, we must also be vigilant about the environment into which the individual has been recruited and the additional expectations an appointment of this nature is likely to attract, from white colleagues keen to add credibility to their diversity-related work and from people of colour either hoping to reach similar points in their careers or desperate for advice about particular workplace challenges.[5] There are colour-coded expectations placed upon this appointee that extend beyond the mere fulfilment of their job description.[6]

The counternarrative in this chapter charts the tensions which emerge between the lead character Nigel Small and our antagonist Sally Cartwright. Note the difference between Sally's words as framed in the press release and her actual behaviour. Press releases are useful mechanisms or performative tools which often set out how the institution *wants* to appear rather than the stark reality. Even though Sally's role as Chief Executive ought to dictate that she will not be involved in the day-to-day operations of Nigel's programme, she uses her position, and therefore power, to repeatedly undermine and disregard his authority. His efforts to respond professionally, by speaking with her, by designing an alternative cost-cutting proposal, are ignored.

Nigel and Sally's racialized and gendered identities are important throughout. Their interactions and the challenges revealed by them tell us something of the dynamics and culture of the institution. As with Robert in Chapter 2, *The Meeting*, we learn who and what is tolerated and who is not, irrespective of who is wrong or right and irrespective of who is doing their job badly or well. Again, as I have argued throughout this book, these practices reveal the contours of power and who has it – and refuses to relinquish it – and who does not.[7]

So far, my interrogation of the way in which power relations have played out between Sally and Nigel has centred on their communication surrounding the exhibition. The *subject* of the exhibition, and their respective roles and identities in relation to it, is also important. Even though she has no substantive knowledge of slavery, race or racism, this does not prevent or indeed limit Sally's confidence in speaking out on the issue or making decisions about it. Again, we could dismiss this as individual arrogance or naivety but, as with Digbeth Winthorpe-Brown's misguided declarations about positive discrimination and racial categorization in Chapter 3, *Members Only*, Sally's actions can be understood as emblematic of whiteness. Her actions and presumption of superior knowledge work to subjugate Nigel and render him impotent despite his experience, position and knowledge. And, like Digbeth, she imposes her own criteria of racial credibility and competence via, in this case, her working-class roots and Ghanaian mentee.

As I explained at the start of this book, the fictional accounts are informed by research findings, experiences shared with me during the course of my career and by publicly available information recorded, for example, by the media. In this vein, I draw this chapter to a close by sharing the words of the Ghanaian-Scottish architect Lesley Lokko who, at the start of 2020, took up a post as Dean at the Bernard and Anne Spitzer School of Architecture at the City College of New York in Manhattan.[8] She tendered her resignation after less than a year:

> My decision to leave Spitzer after less than a year is fairly straightforward: I was not able to build enough support to be able to deliver on either my promise of change, or my vision of it. The reasons why are more complex. Part of it has to do with COVID-19 and the rapid lockdown, which occurred after only three months in post. It's hard enough to build social capital in a new place without having to do it over Zoom. Part of it too has to do with the wider inflexibility of U.S. academic structures. In an incredibly bureaucratic and highly-regulated context, change is as much administrative as it is conceptual. The lack of meaningful support – not lip service, of which there's always a surfeit – meant my workload was absolutely crippling. No job is worth one's life and at times I genuinely feared for my own. Race is never far from the surface of any situation in the U.S. Having come directly from South Africa, I wasn't prepared for the way it manifests in the U.S. and quite simply, I lacked

the tools to both process and deflect it. The lack of respect and empathy for Black people, especially Black women, caught me off guard, although it's by no means unique to Spitzer. I suppose I'd say in the end that my resignation was a profound act of self-preservation.[9]

8: A Special Kind of Madness

The psychoanalysts say that nothing is more traumatizing
for the young child than his encounters with what is
rational. I would personally say that for a man whose only
weapon is reason there is nothing more neurotic than contact with unreason.

Frantz Fanon (1967: 89)

Scenario 1 – The Engagement Party

The argument started long before they reached the car.

'You're just not getting it. We always let them off the hook.
Well, this evening should have been an exception.'

'Philip, I do get it but you can't just lash out and destroy
their party.'

'It's not a question of lashing out. They always put us
down and treat us as though we're second-class citizens and
we lap it up in the spirit of being polite. We're puppets! They
have us on a string. Jackie was right to question him.'

'I disagree. She should have known what he would say.
Why ask the question if you're not prepared to hear a
response that you're uncomfortable with?'

They had reached the car. Philip climbed in on the driver's
side and, in his frustration, pulled the door closed a little too
heavily. After throwing her handbag on to the back seat, Vivian slid in on the passenger's side.

'Oh come on! How would she have known? The man had it coming, Vivian. He was an ignorant, arrogant bastard.'

'Yes, but he already told her earlier in the evening that this was the first time he had attended an event with so many Black people and that it had taken him a moment to adjust, so she should have known how he would respond when she asked about his website.'

'For God's sake, what the hell is he adjusting to? We don't have two heads.'

'Philip, you are not listening to me.'

'I *am* listening to you and you're wrong. Jackie was perfectly entitled to ask the question. Simon should have known better given who was sat around him to say what he said. What kind of arrogance makes you believe that you can say something as racist as that – at an event with Black people – and not get pushback? He's a racist bastard!'

'I am not saying that it wasn't racist, what I am saying is that Jackie should have known better based on how he behaved earlier.'

'But it isn't her job to compromise herself for his racism. *He* should have been more circumspect based on who he was sitting with. As I say, he is at an event with Black people, for goodness sake. It is for *him* to shut his damn mouth and leave his racist crap at home.'

'Philip. This was Mark and Alison's engagement party. We were all there to celebrate them and their union. This isn't about Simon, and it isn't about Jackie. It was about Mark and Alison and making the evening special for them.'

Philip kissed his teeth.

'Did you hear that man make the evening special? Did you? When he said he could never have Black women model shoes for his website because it is high end, and his brand is about elegance and the shoes wouldn't sell – was that special? Did it make you feel special as a Black woman? Damn racist . . .'

'Look, I agree what he said was out of order but the fact remains Jackie shouldn't have asked the question. You saw how the temperature of the conversation changed. It started to get heated. We both know how Jackie is – she was ready to go for him.'

'And she should have! At the end of the day, when we go to their events, we know how to behave. We don't make dumb-ass comments about white people even if we've gone through shit with them. We know how to play the game. And what you have here is a white man who is so up himself that he thinks he can come into our space and dis-respect us. Worse still, most of us act like duppy and bend and flex and kowtow to keep the white man happy – even at our own events!'

'So, what would you have her do? Cuss him out? Cause a big disturbance? Philip, you're talking foolishness because you're vex. You know that it was only because Sandrine stepped in that the whole thing didn't blow up and spoil the evening.'

'It is not foolishness, you know, Vivian. "The black man has two dimensions. One with his fellows, the other with the white man. A Negro behaves differently with a white man and with another Negro. That this self-division is a *direct result of colonialist subjugation* is beyond question . . ." '

Vivian sighed and turned to look out of the window into the summer's night. She knew better than to try to reason with Philip when he began citing Baldwin.

Scenario 2 – The Wheels on the Bus

The wheels on the bus go round and round
Round and round
Round and round
The wheels on the bus go round and round
All through the town

Original by Verna Hills, 1939

Are you sitting comfortably? Then let us begin.

Once upon a time, not very long ago, there was a Black woman called Isabelle. Isabelle was very smart. In fact, she had gone to one of the best schools that her Nigerian immigrant parents could afford. When she finished school, she attended a Russell Group university (surviving as one of only three Black students in her year group[1]) and achieved an upper second in Politics, Philosophy and Economics.

Isabelle became a managing director – and the first Black woman to hold such a role – at one of the world's oldest banks. Her social life and tastes extended far beyond her working-class roots. She holidayed in Tuscany and Turks & Caicos, bought expensive artisan coffee at the tiny coffee shack next to the train station and, each year, placed an order with Vosges Haut-Chocolat in Chicago scheduled to arrive just in time for Easter. And though she could switch into Nigerian pidgin at the drop of a hat, gesticulating and fixing her face in a manner that would have made any Naija Aunty proud, her accent was saturated with a level of English refinement that would have not been out of place in that season's highly acclaimed period drama.

Isabelle counted amongst her circle an enviable array of well-connected, hard-working Black and Asian friends and a healthy sprinkling of white ones, some of whom hailed from her days at university and others she had met during the course of her career. In short, Isabelle embodied the type of upward mobility that politicians would trip over themselves to claim their policies, though lacking any actual reference to race, had enabled.

It is Wednesday afternoon. Isabelle has arranged to meet her friend (one of her white friends) Laura at a teashop in a backstreet in Richmond. Though relatively modest in size, the teashop accommodates five of the latest range of inexplicably large high-end buggies. Laura's own child – Sammy – is ensconced in his UPPAbaby Vista pushchair chewing contentedly on the corner of a now soggy and much deformed mini-croissant. It has been a long time since the two women last saw each other and there is much to catch up on including Laura's experiences as a stay-at-home mum and thoughts about having another baby, and Isabelle's ongoing search for a stable partner. Three oat milk lattes and two flat whites later, they make their way slowly to the nearest children's playground stopping intermittently to share their appreciation of a dress or some other item of clothing on display in the shop windows.

They reach the park. Finally released from his pram, Sammy runs to the other side of the play area. Laura's eyes follow him and she calls out encouraging words as he reaches a wooden blue and green boat and begins to climb gingerly up the steps on its side. Isabelle watches Sammy and also smiles.

'It's amazing to think that just five years ago we were following you up the aisle in the Cotswolds,' she recollects.

'Isn't it? I've been so lucky, Isabelle. Dominic is a wonderful father . . . I mean, work keeps him really busy but he spends every minute he can get with Sammy and always calls if he can't make it home in time to say goodnight. That summer in the Cotswolds – the wedding – does seem like it was such a long time ago now. The day was a blur but you . . . you were fantastic.' She looks at Isabelle briefly before turning back to check on Sammy. 'Thank you again for being my right-hand bridesmaid.'

Isabelle returns a warm smile as they both reflect on Laura's wedding day.

'It was brilliant, and it was an honour to be there for you. Anyway, how is Dominic? I think I last saw him at that dinner party you had last year.'

'He—Sammy, be careful, darling – use the stairs, don't jump. Dominic is well. His boss loves him but I think secretly he has had enough. He isn't really being stimulated—'

'Mummy, Mummy – look at me!'

Sammy runs with arms outstretched, making aeroplane noises as he pelts across the playground to the next kiddies' installation that has caught his attention.

'That's great, darling!' Laura calls after him. 'You're doing really well.' She turns back to Isabelle. 'Where was I? Yes, to be honest, Isabelle, I think he is getting a little bored. He hasn't said so explicitly but . . .'

Sammy climbs up the steps attached to a single storey yellow and red wooden bus and, chattering contentedly to himself, makes his way to the driver's seat.

'Mummy! Bruuumm, bruuum! Look at me, Mummy!'

'Yes, that's lovely, Sammy.'

'Bruuuum, brumm!'

Sammy looks left and right repeatedly and suddenly points at Isabelle.

'Oh no, look out, Mummy! Mummy, look out! Look out for the Black in-twu-da! Watch out – the Black in-twu-da, Mummy!'

Both women freeze.

Isabelle turns cold. Nausea floats at the bottom of her stomach churning uncomfortably with the coffee she'd consumed earlier, as she works to reconcile what she has heard. 'Black intruder?'

Laura doesn't look at her at first and then, in a voice strained with the effort of attempting to sound light and breezy, finally breaks the silence.

'I . . . goodness knows where he got that from. I . . . it . . . it clearly wasn't from us.'

Isabelle cannot speak. She is still in shock. She stares at Laura and then turns her head slowly back to look at Sammy who, oblivious to the discomfort he has caused, continues to play happily, steering the bus diligently across imaginary busy streets.

'Look, perhaps we should go,' Laura says and awkwardly begins to pack the UPPAbaby bag with Sammy's belongings.

Scenario 3 – The Letter of Complaint

Dear Ms Cartwright

Today I attended the private view of Slavery Uncovered at the National Centre for the Creative Arts which was billed as a 'unique and ground-breaking exposé of the Transatlantic Slave Trade and its continued legacy'. As a Black woman of Caribbean heritage, whose own ancestors were slaves, I was appalled and deeply insulted by every aspect of the exhibition including the welcome speech by the African American artist

Sanctity Blue. For the purposes of this letter, I focus on three key issues: the soundscape installation, the canteen slave food 'pop-up' and your choice of speaker for the evening.

First, it is unclear to me how a soundscape installation of a slave being beaten constitutes an exposé. Rather, visitors are subjected to what can only be described as the audible pornification of violence against Black bodies. The text and visual imagery that accompany the soundscape offer no warning to visitors – and moreover zero sensitivity to those of Black African and Caribbean heritage – about the potentially triggering nature of what they will hear. In fact, the text seems to revel in detailing forms of control and violence perpetuated by white slave masters with zero examination of the many occasions where slaves exercised agency through revolt or rebellion. Further, by centring on white slave owners you have only served to recentre whiteness and a narrow portrayal of slavery for your audience – a demographic which I understand tends to be white, middle class and able bodied.

Second, I took profound offence at the canteen 'pop-up' which featured staff, who I understand to be contractors, dressed in what was described as 'authentic slave attire'. I spoke with one of the servers who told me how the company – Deluxe Catering – had worked tirelessly alongside NCCA for several months to design both the food menu and ensure the raggedy, dirty appearance of the outfits would still meet Health & Hygiene standards but that no similar exercise had taken place, to her knowledge, to test the palatability of the actual idea with Black and Brown people. To present and seek to reimagine the food consumed by slaves in the form of canapés and bowl food, stripped bare of the context of the dietary compromises they were

157

compelled to make, reveals a level of disconnected bourgeois privilege and cultural consumption that frankly is hard to stomach.

Finally, the choice of Sanctity Blue to headline the evening can only be described as short-sighted, insensitive and out of touch with the groundswell of opinion and experiences of campaign groups and racially minoritized communities here in the UK. Any cursory search of her work reveals her to be opposed to any detailed examination of racism that focuses on structural inequalities and indeed overlooks the role that those in positions of power play in perpetuating this. While her highly controversial training programme 'The Rhythm of Love' has been gaining traction since the violent racist attack against Samuel Adewale last year, she has decried Black Lives Matter as a terrorist movement and argued that love, kindness and understanding will heal racism as opposed to any theoretically based argument that focuses on the role that white people play in perpetuating racial injustice. In a recent piece for the *Spectator*, Blue argued that 'factors intrinsic to the Black community' and an obsession with 'defeatist self-centredness' were responsible for our lack of societal progression as opposed to racism. She stated that Black men prefer drugs and guns over any willingness to properly father their children and that Black women are more concerned with hairstyles (weaves and extensions being high in her sights while ignoring her own blonde shoulder-length wig) and fake nails than possessing the ambition to fight workplace challenges and succeed. In short, other than being high profile, from the US and having completed the UK press and private club speaker circuit, Sanctity Blue cannot in any way be described as well placed to headline an exhibition framed as presenting an honest deconstruction of slavery. I did raise my objections about Ms Blue with one of the Centre's managers on the evening and was told that NCCA 'works hard to include the voices of marginalized groups in its work' and given that Ms Blue is African American and in high demand they had considered securing her booking 'an achievement'.

I would like to know:

1 Who decided that Sanctity Blue would make an appropriate speaker and why?
2 What effort was made to find Black British talent (that is, someone more au fait and accomplished to speak to the full complexities of racism) to headline your evening?
3 Who financed this exhibition, who sanctioned it and what ethical process did the proposal go through?
4 If this proposal was discussed and approved by a board or review panel, I would like to know a) their ethnic backgrounds and b) their knowledge base and experience in matters of racial justice.
5 Whether a consultation process was carried out with any charity or advisory groups specializing in the Transatlantic Slave Trade or, more broadly, with issues of decolonization, identity and racism within the cultural heritage sector?

I look forward to your response.
Ava Carter

Dear Ms Carter
I write in response to your letter of 6 July.

The National Centre for the Creative Arts was established in 1968 under the Commonwealth Integration Act to ensure that 'the experiences and interests of Britain's rich and vibrant past are reflected on our shores'. Since then, NCCA has had twelve Directors each committed to realizing this vision in consultation with our 8,000+ membership. Sally Cartwright joined NCCA at the start of last year as the first woman to lead the institution in its fifty-plus-year history and is the first female Director of any cultural heritage institution in the UK. Ms Cartwright has an extensive track record within the policy and cultural sectors, having successfully led the government's 'Back on Track' campaign which supported over 15,000 unemployed people to get back into work and, prior to that, worked as a senior civil servant across a number of government departments. Her appointment as Director of NCCA confirms our investment in diversity and inclusion and points to our position as leaders within the cultural heritage sector.

We continue to go from strength to strength in our work on diversity. Last year we recruited KLIP – the UK's leading employment consultancy – to simplify our workforce and to carry out an internal audit of diversity and inclusion across the institution. We are currently reviewing their recommendations.

At a programme level, we recently launched 'Up from the Ghetto' – a mentoring scheme pairing talented artists with school pupils from deprived inner-city neighbourhoods and have also commissioned the well-known Black visual artist Freddy 'Uncle Tom' Junior to paint the building in the colours of the Rastafarian movement during this year's Black History Month.[2]

Our Director of Programmes & Commissions has taken an inclusive approach to our work and welcomed a range of contributions and suggestions from our membership. Our new exhibition Slavery Uncovered captures our vision for a 'new diversity of the future' by merging immersive technological advances with uncomfortable historical events to support public engagement and learning. I appreciate Slavery Uncovered did not meet your expectations in terms of its content, but this does not sit in line with its wider reception. Mere days after it opened, *The Tabloid* described it as a 'fascinating insight into the past' and the Rt Hon. Douglas Adebayo MP, who you will know is himself of Nigerian extraction, hailed it as a 'thought-provoking reflection of a Britain that once was but is no more'.

On receipt of your letter, I also reviewed our advertising and marketing content about the exhibition and remain of the view that it reflects a fair and accurate representation of historical events.

Sincerely,
Adam Gilchrist
Director of Communications

A guide to writing an institutional response to a charge of racism

1 Do not respond yourself. Ensure your Director of Communications or direct report replies.
2 Under no circumstances should you engage with the central premise of the complaint directly. Spend between 90 per cent and 95 per cent of the letter discussing other matters (see #3) and include just one or two sentences on the central issue.
3 Set out the background and history of your organization, the initiative or related policy in order to assert your status, authority and legitimacy over both the complainant and the content of the complaint.

4 Document how you have excelled in some (it does not matter which) broad area of diversity and inclusion. Stating statistics and naming awards will be well placed here. Ignore the fact that the letter of complaint pertains solely to racial justice. That is a mere technicality.

5 Keep the tone perfunctory and aloof. Do not empathize, offer an apology or be apologetic.

6 If the complainant appears educated and well informed, increase the level of your authority by using legalistic terms such as 'for the avoidance of doubt'; 'reasonably'; 'with due regard to'.

7 In short, accept no ownership of or engagement with the complaint and treat the entire process as if it is a PR exercise.

8 If, despite these tactics, you are compelled to investigate the matter (for example, if the individual explicitly cites your complaints policy), then make sure it is carried out internally and always falls in your favour. By this point, it is pretty much guaranteed you will have exhausted the complainant, or they will have become preoccupied with other matters.

———

This chapter has focused on the assessments and calculations people of colour are compelled to make when faced with everyday racism. In addition to the initial emotional response – shock, hurt, humiliation, irritation, anger – that such incidents provoke, being subjected to racism also means acknowledging, if not engaging with, the irrationality and contradictions that accompany it. Decisions must also be made about whether and indeed how to respond to the perpetrator.

In *The Engagement Party*, Vivian and Philip offer very different responses to Simon's aggression. Vivian is conciliatory in her reasoning, seeking peace for the hosts and the greater good of the evening. Rather than criticize Simon, she instead centres her attentions on Jackie, accusing her of being in the wrong for having provoked him. Jackie, she insists, understands the ways in which whiteness operates and therefore should adopt the moral high ground and ignore him. This, ostensibly, might be a logical response – after all it is impossible to respond to every slight or putdown – and saying or doing nothing could be seen as a healthier course of action. In reality, the act of ignoring is still an act. It is a *reaction* since, by default, it necessitates recognition of precisely that which is to be avoided and so demands of the individual a suppression or pretence either of the fact that the offence took place or of its consequences.

Philip, by contrast, concentrates wholly on Simon and his remarks, offering no latitude for behaviours he considers disrespectful. Philip is angry not just because of what was said but because Simon had the temerity to utter them to Black people. As Philip correctly points out, Black people often find themselves in the company of white people and 'know how to play the game'. That is, they know how to be civil despite the racism they experience and despite knowing that it sits below the thin surface of most interactions with whites. What he overlooks, of course, is that the rules operate differently for the oppressed compared with the privileged. The oppressed must understand and work to the rules if they are to be tolerated and given the opportunity to progress. The privileged make the rules. This is also reflected by the fact that despite their differing responses and reading of the incident, it is Simon – or more accurately whiteness – and not Vivian and Philip's enjoyment of the evening which remains centre stage.[3]

Here we begin to see something of the difficulties of maintaining a humane existence within spaces that are racially mixed in this way. Such moments carry risk because there is always the possibility of being subjected to offence and the possibility that the white person will respond with denial or defensiveness if challenged. As such, these incidents, however fleeting, carry the characteristics of emotional abuse: the need to self-regulate, to self-edit, to remain watchful in the presence of white people because of the offence they have caused and because of what they can and are known to do.[4]

The visceral nature of this precarity is laid bare in *The Wheels on the Bus* in which Laura's son Sammy repeats the words of caution that he has heard voiced by adults. Sammy is a young child, therefore we are not seeking to judge him. However, the juxtaposition of the playground setting and the child-like innocence that infuses the unexpected bluntness of his words and the way he points accusatorily at Isabelle serve to abruptly disrupt the nostalgic cosiness of the conversation between his mother and her friend. Isabelle is caught in a state of *cognitive dissonance*, a term used by psychologists to capture the mental discomfort and instability felt when confronted by two contradictory states, sets of belief or information. What we actually see or bear witness to is her emotional shock.

Finally, let's turn to *The Letter of Complaint* in which Ava Carter sets out her concerns about the Slavery Uncovered exhibition. Her letter, though addressed to the CEO, is answered by the Director of Communications. Comms teams are one of the ways institutions work to hold constant and manage their self-image, norms and culture. These mechanisms of control operate like a tightly oiled machine whose sole purpose is to protect the institution even if it sometimes means constructing fluid interpretations of what everyone involved knows to be the truth. These protective processes are characterized by detached forms of communication that work to create distance and re-establish boundaries between the organization and those who are perceived as a threat to it.[5]

A more humane or sincere response driven by empathy, compassion and reflexivity might be sufficient to reassure the complainant that their concerns have been taken seriously, but such reactions are often seen to imply an admission of guilt and, as such, increase the likelihood of placing the organization at risk from poor press or social media coverage or even legal action. Since protection and defence are the principal goals, the complainant becomes dehumanized, that is, treated not as a sensing or hurt human being but as an inconvenience or threat to be resolved or eliminated. The complainant, as opposed to the issues they raised, becomes the problem.[6] Adam's letter is not just a reflection of how the organization handles complaints but is also indicative of its engagement with race. There are similarities here with Sally's handling of the exhibition and her treatment of Nigel. Each of these acts retain and convey important data about each individual and the organization's racial maturity.

Interlude: The Facemask

> [. . .] I have only lived as me, a person who regularly has to negotiate conscious and unconscious dismissal, erasure, disrespect, and abuse [. . .]
>
> Claudia Rankine[1]

Today I watched a video that had been posted on LinkedIn.

It was posted by a Black man, here in the UK, and showed security men from a well-known department store grabbing him by the wrist, pulling him and shouting at him that he had not paid for two suitcases that were also visible in the shot.

I watched with the lens I encourage my students to adopt: take nothing at face value and always ask questions both of the scene and what *appears* to be happening and, crucially, of yourself. Do not pre-judge. So, while the Black man shouted back and bodies tussled back and forth, I told myself that I did not yet have evidence to indicate whether or not he had indeed paid, nor did I have evidence to indicate whether or not the security men were correct in their accusation.

I kept watching.

The security men (one is white wearing a Covid-precautionary facemask, the other is Asian and without a facemask) repeatedly ask the Black man if he has paid, insisting that management said he had not. While they do this, they continue to hold and pull at his wrist and tug at the items he is alleged to have taken. The Black man is shouting, telling

166

them to let go of him. The Asian man accuses him of having a tantrum. The Black man's facemask is on the ground. He shouts that of course he has paid. Two additional security personnel (one man, one woman, both white and wearing facemasks) join the group and there is further disjointed movement of the camera and more raised voices as the new security man tells him his facemask is on the floor and he should be wearing it. During this, the Asian man receives confirmation via his radio that the Black man hasn't paid for the items. The woman shouts at him to calm down. The Black man shouts that he is not wearing a mask that has been on the floor and continues to insist that he is being treated badly.

The shouting, pulling and jostling continue. People – other shoppers – stare. Whether the Black man has paid or not, it is unsettling.

Then the Asian man receives more information on his radio. It turns out that the man *has* paid. The Asian man states this news out loud and then simply walks off back to the store.

At this point, I realize that my attempts at objectivity have waned. I am upset. The Black man is offered no apology. There is no explanation. No one helps put his belongings together nor reassures him in anyway. No one does anything to rebalance or seek to address the indignity of his having been mishandled, embarrassed and accused so publicly.

I replay the section several times in order to locate an apology that I must have missed. I must have missed an apology. I must have. I am upset, I tell myself. Let me rewatch that part more closely.

There is no apology.

It is unedifying.

I feel sick.

I am angry.

I continue to watch.

The Black man is agitated. He is angry. He is shouting at the security guards to tell everyone who has witnessed them apprehend him, witnessed them mishandle him and accuse him that he has indeed paid, that they must say it. They must say it to the camera.

The original security men walk back into the shop with the Black man still calling after them to come back.

The Asian man who received the message that the Black man paid has now reached the store entrance. Eventually, he turns around and says: 'Yo' listen, I'm man enough to say it: you've paid.'

I am angry. I am upset because still there is no apology. There is no attempt to explain the error and how it was made. There is no attempt to reinstate the dignity that has been stripped from the Black man.

The Black man continues to shout and make known the injustice he has been served.

Even while he does this, the remaining security staff continue to ask for a receipt.

I am upset.

The woman says as if it is sufficient explanation: 'People make mistakes.'

'No,' says the Black man, 'people are racist.'

His distress is evident. I do not know him but I am with him in his distress.

I know his pain.

Our Blackness – what they do to our Blackness – is our shared pain.

The Black man is shouting that he wants to speak to the General Manager.

A new person appears – a white man in a blue-grey suit with a lanyard dangling around his neck. He stands talking with the remaining security personnel. The Black man approaches him:

INNOCENT MAN: Are you the General Manager of [shopping centre]?

DUTY MANAGER: I'm a Duty Manager of [shopping centre]. You won't be speaking to the General Manager. So, you can speak to me or no one. It's up to you.

I am confused. I do not understand the reason for the manager's hostility to this innocent man. My heart breaks.

INNOCENT MAN: I want to speak to the General Manager.

DUTY MANAGER: It's not happening.

Is this how to speak to a customer who has been wrongfully accused of stealing by your security staff?

INNOCENT MAN: It's not what?

DUTY MANAGER: It's not happening.

INNOCENT MAN: So, is the General Manager in or not in?

DUTY MANAGER: You're not speaking to the General Manager. You can speak to me, I'm the Duty Manager.

INNOCENT MAN: Cool, I'd like to speak to the General Manager.

DUTY MANAGER: It's not happening tonight.

I watch this exchange and note the Duty Manager's manner, how he is standing, his choice of words and the way in which he says them. He is defensive. His tone is not apologetic. He is not seeking to pacify or to understand. Why is he acting like this?

The innocent Black man begins to ask a series of questions about who the Duty Manager reports into. The Duty Manager answers but is not particularly forthcoming or helpful. He interrupts to ask where this is going. I know where it is going, and I am not even there. I know not because my academic mind tells me but because my experiences as a Black woman tell me. I know that the innocent Black man is seeking to establish the Duty Manager's seniority within the organizational structure. Why? There is a possibility, however small, that the person in charge will take more seriously any potential complaints and concerns about reputational damage than someone lower down in the chain.

The Black man continues to talk. He becomes calmer as he basically gives a free lecture about the way in which stereotyping and racism work. He references the African American man George Floyd who was murdered, in May 2020, by a white policeman following the accusation that he used a counterfeit $20 bill.

The Duty Manager admits his attitude at the start was wrong.

I think I am crying but am so frozen with disbelief – despite all that I have seen and heard – that I cannot be sure.

I write a carefully thought-through comment which I post to LinkedIn about how the store and shopping centre staff missed many opportunities to manage the situation better and to treat the accused man with humanity and respect.

I write this message and say nothing of the existential pain I feel in my core having borne witness, yet again, to the indignities of having to negotiate society when Black.

9: Default to White

It had been just two weeks since Nigel handed in his notice at the National Centre for the Creative Arts and his friends – and the gym – were bearing the brunt of his anger and indignation. He'd spent a considerable amount of time on the phone cussing. He had cussed to his sister who lived in Birmingham, who vowed that she and her family would never again grace the institution with their presence as long as Cartwright remained in charge. He cussed to his closest friend Miguel who, upon hearing of Nigel's experiences, cussed in Spanish. And he also cussed to his Jamaican postman (albeit a wholly more restrained version) who had seen the article in the newspaper and asked how he was getting on. And each of the people he had cussed to shared the news with their friends and families and, despite not knowing each other personally, were in collective agreement that trying to get ahead in this country as a Black person was hard work. For all his talk, the White Man (or Woman) did not want you to succeed; after all, look at what had happened to Nigel Small and to countless others they knew.

Tonight, Nigel was at a dinner party – a casual laidback affair – at the home of his friend Samantha in a leafy suburb of outer London. The guest of honour was one Professor Sherman J. Taylor who was renowned not just in the well-connected upper middle-class echelons of elite African Americans, with their endless list of sororities and fraternities of which they were (mostly) so proud, but amongst the small network of Black British middle classes too.

Samantha had spent most of her career as a teacher and had fought and clawed her way to the brink of headship before the weight of evening and weekend working, the endless paper-work and marking (which always took much longer than their Head said), the endless government interventions, the tedious form-filling that inevitably came with it and a string of unsup-portive line managers had taken its toll. She had been taken away by those good old men in white coats for a brief stay in a local hospital unit while she recovered from her breakdown. Her daughter Thea, now twenty-one and living in Paris while she finished her PhD, had kept dear the letter her mother had written to her at the time which explained what was happening to her. It would serve as her guide through life, she said, a reminder of what institutions can do to your soul. Her mother now ran a small online business selling handmade leather goods. The creativity and ability to work for herself far away from institutions and from line managers who made flimsy promises about diversity that they failed to uphold had restored Samantha to her former warm, contented self.

Somewhere between the main course and dessert, the conversation turned to the subject of young people, follow-ing a news item that morning which had announced that a seventeen-year-old influencer was preparing to sue the fash-ion label Sexy & Cute because they had failed to issue their Autumn collection, which she had been contracted to model, in the right shade of cherry blossom pink as had been agreed. While she conceded with some reluctance that the collection was indeed pink, the shade did not complement the blusher from the latest make-up range by Never Too Much that she was also contracted to wear that season.

JENNIFER: Personally, I blame the parents. I do! The level of sheer entitlement and quickness to scream they are being treated unfairly in the face of what are either completely ridiculous wants or entirely normal life challenges ... I mean for goodness sake ... cherry blossom pink – I ask you!

NIGEL: Oh come on, when they're that age what can parents do? Remember they have the internet now. It's not like when we were kids when we either saw each other in person or, if lucky, managed to sneak to use the phone to speak with one another when our parents' backs were turned.

There was laughter and nostalgic nods of agreement at this.

JENNIFER: I hear you but, ultimately, it's still down to the parents. Take JBL, for example. Last month, I agreed I would mentor a young Black girl from a local comprehensive. You know the kind of thing – show them the ropes, give her career advice and so on. She seemed relatively switched on and I initially thought I would take her under my wing when the two months ended ... you know, act like an Aunty maybe and support her through university, give life advice and so on. You know she hadn't been there for two minutes when she started demanding things: she wanted a dedicated parking space WITH her name on a sign above it. She'd noticed the members of the board had them, she said. She wanted business cards. And when I said no and explained that cards were only for employees, she took herself off to the local printers to get some mocked up herself! What set her back was that she didn't have access to our logo but that didn't stop her asking for it

173

and then going into a strop when Marketing said no. And then yesterday, she asked whether she could have her own office, that she wasn't 'really feeling the hot desking thing, you know'! Now if that level of damn arrogance and self-entitlement isn't down to shabby parenting, I don't know what is!

Both Nigel and Samantha's eyes stretched with incredulity, although Samantha remained reluctant to condemn either young people themselves or their parents:

SAMANTHA: Well, maybe she just doesn't know any better, but with your guidance . . .

JENNIFER: Girl, please! You know these parents – all labels and credit cards. It's no wonder that our children turn out as they do!

NIGEL: Well, your true colours are really coming out this evening, Jen [*he laughed*]. You're not the secret love child of one Douglas Adebayo MP, are you?

Jennifer pretended to fix him with a stony glare but amicably joined him in laughter.

JENNIFER: Now *that* is one Black man who has really forgotten who he is! Always cussing Black people for not [*she put on an exaggerated posh voice*] 'making the most of the opportunities this absolutely excellent country has to offer'.

Samantha laughed at Jen's terrible impersonation.

SAMANTHA: Adebayo's not Black – not Black Black.

She turned to Professor Sherman to explain who Adebayo was and the kind of arguments he had made in Parliament.

Professor Sherman, a man with a warm avuncular disposition, listened and nodded sagely.

PROFESSOR: We got those kind of folk back home in the US. A little *too* integrated, we say! Lost their way on the way up [*he chuckled to himself*], but Nigel, I hear you been having some trouble with the white folk at that museum. What they call it now? The Museum of Intercultural . . .?

NIGEL: The National Centre for Creative Arts. It has been hell.

He proceeded to share an outline of what had happened; his account met with the odd 'right' and 'uhhuh' from Professor Sherman and sighing and shaking of the head from the women. When he had finished, there was a brief silence which was broken by Samantha, who had been aware of events as they unfolded as Nigel had called her every evening after work to complain and ask for advice:

SAMANTHA: It really is madness. I mean, I thought they wanted to widen their membership. I used to have meetings in their canteen – before this nonsense with Nigel – and it's mainly mums with strollers and well-off pensioners. All white.

NIGEL: They do – well, they say they do but they don't want to do anything to upset any of their existing members and are absolutely petrified about losing any of their patrons. They are a key source of their income and obviously also act as ambassadors for the Centre.

JENNIFER: Are you serious? They treat you like shit because they're scared of their patrons? I bet they don't even know who *you* are. Who are *they* anyway? Anyone we might know?

Professor Sherman continued to listen attentively, only pausing occasionally in his ruminations to pour himself some more wine.

> NIGEL: I can't remember all their names ... Elisabeth Carrington-Smyth, formerly of CIRCLE banking group; Elgar Brunswick, CEO of Brunswick Enterprises; and Digbeth Winthorpe-somebody or other, some obnoxious big wig who spends most of his time making deals from the dusty dark corners of his private members' club, so I hear. There are a couple of others. I forget their names.
>
> SAMANTHA: All white, I assume?

Nigel gave her a look that provided sufficient affirmation to her question.

> NIGEL: And of course, there's Sally Cartwright herself [*he pronounced in a voice dripping with scornful dramatic flourish*], the archetypal White Working-Class Woman Made Good who gets racism better than *any* Black person! Who, because of her own deprived childhood in the backstreets of Liverpool – back before it was awarded European City of Culture status – *knows* what it is to suffer, to compromise. [*He clutched his hands to his chest in the kind of over-exaggerated gesture of despair embraced by the heroines of those black and white movies of the 1940s.*] She *knows* what it is to work your way up from a place of disadvantage. Sally Cartwright IS our biggest ally!
>
> JENNIFER: Ahhh, the self-appointed white ally! Don't you just love them?

They fell silent for a moment as they each reflected on their own careers and the barriers they had encountered en route:

the CEO who publicly declared his commitment to advancing racial justice, while ignoring the disproportionate number of Black and Asian people leaving his organization; the white female line manager (and sometimes the odd Asian one) who made every effort to promote their own work and achievements but failed to promote the outstanding work of their underrepresented pool of Black staff; the endless examples of having to fight for due recognition during appraisals and promotion rounds.

SAMANTHA [*sighing*]: Can I offer anyone dessert? Nigel? Professor?

Jennifer shook her head. Nigel and Professor Sherman indicated they would have something in a short while.

PROFESSOR: You know, as dire as this is, none of this should surprise us.

They looked at him quizzically.

SAMANTHA: What do you mean?
PROFESSOR: Well, we scratch our heads, cuss to one another about how they treat us, but we forget, ultimately it's all about power. Power is the real problem. And I know it will make some folk here in England uncomfortable – it's upset folk back in the US – but ultimately this is about how people who have historically had or taken power, hold on to power. And whether we like it or not, it's white folk who have power. Now, they may regale us every so often about some random Black or Brown person who has made it to the top of some organization as being a symbol of change and progress but we know how this stuff operates.

NIGEL: Go on.

PROFESSOR: Well, if you don't mind me saying, let's look at your situation. You got yourself a smart Black man, on top of his game, making waves and knowledgeable about race – well, right away you got yourself a problem. [*He chuckled dryly.*] First of all, you're isolated – how many other senior Black folk were you working with at your museum? And when I say Black, I mean 'kinfolk', not those who are just *incidentally* Black like your Douglas chap . . . that Minister of Parliament. What you say his name was?

JENNIFER [*laughing*]: Adebayo.

PROFESSOR: Right. Douglas Adebayo. I don't mean those kinda folk, I mean regular Black folk who got their wits about them.

NIGEL: It was just me. I mean, there were some Black staff but more at entry level. One Asian guy on the next tier down.

PROFESSOR: Right, so that's your first problem: you've got no one in your corner who can either school you about how this Arts Centre and this woman deal with race or support your cause. You're already weak. Second, why didn't they already have Black folk at senior levels when y'all got talented Black folk right here in London and also in that other place I visited – Bir-ming-ham? That alone is a red flag. And let's not take on any of that 'you gotta start somewhere' shit! The question we need to be asking ourselves is: how is it possible in this day and age, with all your equalities legislation and white folk telling you left, right and centre how committed they are to change, that the problem is still this bad? [*He paused and looked at each of them in turn to ensure he had their full attention.*] So, here's the real issue: they don't really want change.

His dinner companions eyed him sceptically.

SAMANTHA: I don't understand. What are you saying?

PROFESSOR: Okay, let me break it down for you. White folk are in power, right. You got Nigel coming in with all his big ideas for change, about how to make better shows, bring in money, get more Black folk in the audience . . . his problem? His problem isn't just coming up with excellent ideas, the problem is that he has got to convince white folk to feel comfortable with those ideas and to resource them. And when I say comfortable, it's not just a question of convincing them about the *viability* of a project, but what you're also doing – what you also need to do – is make a case why *your* interpretation and solution to *their* race problem is one they should sign up to. Now isn't that something?

In other words, you also have to appeal to *their* interpretation of how *they* perceive racism, which, of course, by implication not only includes them as white people but generally will be at odds with how we – as the recipients, if you will, of racism – want to eradicate it. It doesn't matter what *you* think, how expert you are or what your personal experience is, white people will only sanction anti-racism initiatives that are palatable to *their* perception of how they define the problem of race and how they see themselves as white people.

And let me tell you this, it is a rare white person who will sanction an initiative that either makes him . . . or her . . . uncomfortable or significantly challenges the status quo and their place in it. They may agree to a little

tweak around the edges, you know – keep things looking pretty and . . . what do you all call it over here . . .
'diverse' with one or two projects with some people of
colour doing some small-scale creative nonsense but
nothing to really disrupt that oh so smoothly running
status quo.

Samantha glanced at Nigel out of the corner of her eye.
What Professor Sherman was saying was a little extreme –
radical even – and she wasn't entirely sure she agreed with
him but right now she was mainly concerned about Nigel
and how he might be feeling in light of the Professor's words;
he hadn't stopped cussing Sally Cartwright or the Centre –
having given each rather unpalatable aliases – since he left a
couple of weeks ago. The Professor continued:

Let me ask you a question: that Adebayo guy, you think
he got to where he is based on sheer talent and academic excellence alone? You think his ideas are better
than yours?

They looked at him expectantly.

Well, let me tell you: the answer is no. He is there
because he makes white folk feel comfortable. It's as
simple as that.

He reached with his fork for a roast potato that had not made
it on to their plates earlier and popped it into his mouth.

JENNIFER: Really? I mean, he says some pretty disparag-
ing things about race which I'm sure makes even some
of the white politicians squirm. In fact—

PROFESSOR: Okay, okay, hear me out. Let me break it down for you. [*He paused to swallow the potato.*]

Institutions aren't simply neutral places with four walls, some offices, computers and phones where we work, get paid and go home. They produce things, be it bank notes, more knowledgeable students, or just good old t-shirts. Now in addition to this, we can't just roll up to those institutions and do what we like. We have to follow guidelines, policies, protocols ... navigate people's insecurities, desires for recognition, bad moods, what is seen as acceptable and not acceptable. That is, they also produce culture – there are cultural norms and values to learn most of which are not written down but which shape the fabric of the institution. Are we in agreement with that?

JENNIFER: Well, yes.

PROFESSOR: Right, so – workers, usually of differing seniority, design and interpret those policies in ways that make sense to their worldview: particular people determine whose grievance will be overturned, whose achievements will be awarded with a gold star during their appraisal and who won't even get a bronze one, whose request for annual leave will be signed off without so much as a second glance and whose won't. And we have enough evidence, from decades of research, to show us that particular groups – that is those who look like the ones running the place – tend to benefit from these processes, those policy interpretations, and certain groups just ain't making it through, as my good man Nigel here has just experienced.[1] Right, Nigel?

NIGEL [*sighing heavily*]: Right.

PROFESSOR: So the odds are that those running these institutions are going to seek out, reward and retain those who they deem to be the best 'fit' – a word I have never liked – with their norms, values and cultures.[2] You all still with me?

They nodded.

JENNIFER: Yes, I can think of a couple of situations at work that sit in line with what you're saying.

PROFESSOR: Right, so this concept of 'fit' extends to race and those who are different in some way from the mainstream – and when I say mainstream, I mean those who . . .

NIGEL: . . . those who have power.

PROFESSOR: Right. [*He chortled magnanimously.*] So, a couple of friends of mine back at UCLA have looked at this in relation to race and they argue that institutions reward those who are *racially palatable* – that is, those who downplay or at least do not accentuate their racial identity.[3] Your Douglas Adebayo types. Whereas you're coming with your funky locks on one side of your head and your innovative projects about race – they call that *racially salient* – you got the white folk scared! And what do people do when they're scared or feel their values or ways of operating are under threat? They hunker down, close ranks and start protecting themselves. And if you won't play ball or make them too uncomfortable? Well, it's either them or you and they got more resources, time and networks than Black folk here in the UK so . . . it's gonna be you . . . us. Unadulterated *organizational protectionism* as I call it.[4]

SAMANTHA: Wow, okay, I hear you but isn't that a bit defeatist? I mean, I know all of us have our stories to tell about these places but there have been some changes . . . some improvements. Right?

Professor Sherman didn't look at her but pondered her question a while before responding.

PROFESSOR: Defeatist? No, ma'am, I'm a realist. You ever find yourself in some grievance or tribunal with these people? You see how they will lie and subvert the truth in a way that will make our ancestors roll in their watery graves. Why? To protect themselves even if it means your downfall, breakdown or ruin. And then with the same hand that has penned some unscrupulous poison about you, they will merrily publish some statement on their intranet or website declaring how committed they are to progressing racial justice. Hell, they will even introduce a mentoring scheme or some such to help the po' underrepresented Black folk and will tell you, mark my words: 'Oh, we don't know why there are so few Black people in our institution. It's a pipeline issue – they're just not coming through. We've been trying *so* hard. Why, we gave them mentoring schemes last year to help their confidence, but we're really stuck now.' Please! [*He looked at Jennifer.*] You lack confidence?

JENNIFER: No sir! [*She laughed and shook her head.*]

PROFESSOR: You?

NIGEL: No. I'm hearing you, Professor.

PROFESSOR: Right. So, white folks are smart. Whatever happens, they have the final say.

SAMANTHA: So . . . well, assuming what you say is true, what do we do?

PROFESSOR: Do? [*He peered over his glasses at her and rubbed his chin thoughtfully, as though it was the first time he had contemplated such a question.*]

Well, we got to get educated, financially astute, historically wise and work collectively. Oh, and in our rush to lay claim to our middle-class comforts, we Bourgeois Blacks need to recognize that there's no meaningful racial justice without bringing poor Black folk with us.

They studied him, sobered by the heaviness of his words. He looked back at them and grinned.

PROFESSOR: We can talk on that next but for now, how about that dessert you mentioned earlier?

SAMANTHA [*stirred from her thoughts*]: Okay. You have a choice — homemade apple crumble with custard or grapefruit and orange granita?

10: Darker than Blue[1]

[. . .] you are a black boy, and you must be responsible for your body in a way that other boys cannot know. Indeed, you must be responsible for the worst actions of other black bodies, which, somehow, will always be assigned to you.

Ta-Nehisi Coates (2015: 71)

The heart of the Black British mother-to-be sinks as she is told she will give birth to a boy child. Fear saturates her soul for she knows that her journey will require extra surveillance, additional protection and more care than would be necessary for any other mother. If she is wise and has the means, she will start thinking about the type of school she wants him to attend, and when he is in secondary school the route that he will have to take home, even if it means moving home to a place further out of the city so that he can be distant from any potential threats. The Black British mother knows from the second he is conceived that her son is in danger.

A Black Mother's Guide to Black Sons Everywhere

1 Always take a receipt if you buy something from a shop.
2 If wearing a hooded top – though it is better if you just never wear one in the first place – never put the hood up.
3 Never wear a baseball cap.

4 Do not meander or browse in a shop. Always go directly for what you want, then leave.

5 Always cross the road when you see a white woman or girl.

6 Never look a white person in the eye.

7 Always look a white person in the eye.

8 Avoid wearing trainers. If going to the gym, wear shoes and change at the gym and then when you've finished training, change back into your shoes.

9 No piercings.

10 No tattoos.

11 No patterns in your hair.

12 Avoid routes that take you within two miles of a council or housing association estate.

13 If you see other Black men, avoid them lest the police think you know each other and that you are part of a gang.

14 Never look at or handle or be in the vicinity of toy or pellet guns.

15 Avoid walking on the street. Ideally get a car.

16 Never buy a high-end car.

17 Know and memorize the different forms of stop and search, i.e. Section 1, Section 23, Section 163, Section 60.

18 If stopped, always ask what grounds you have been stopped on but never show that you have a knowledge of the legislation lest they think you're being uppity and it irritates them.

19 Call police officers 'sir', 'madam' or 'officer' when stopped to show courtesy and minimize any untoward conduct on their part.

20 Don't call officers 'sir' or 'madam' in case they think you're being sarcastic, and the situation escalates.

21 Ask if they have switched on their body worn camera.

22 Even if they have switched on their body worn camera, make sure you record any interaction with them on your phone.

Ignore white society who will tell you:

1 The police are there to protect us all.
2 If you've done nothing wrong, you have nothing to worry about.
3 If you have a complaint, you can contact the Independent Office for Police Conduct.[2]
4 We are all the same, stop making the issue about skin colour.
5 Black people are more likely to be victims of homicide than other groups;[3] stop and search and other police tactics exist to protect you.

The sun makes its way languidly across the breaking dawn sky. The warm air carries that sense of still anticipation before a city properly awakens from its slumber usually only enjoyed by earnest, headphone-clad joggers, sleep-deprived travellers on the way to catch 6 a.m. flights, and those invisible workers – cleaners, healthcare professionals – slumped with fatigue on otherwise empty public transport.

The promise of the heat that will later cast an unwieldy heaviness across the city is already making itself known as the jogger pants up the hill and past the lake. A gentle breeze that offers no relief from the exhaustion of the run rustles through the upmost leaves of the trees that dominate the heath.

She has not reached the point yet, just beyond the clearing, where the ground rises toward the east where a shape hangs loosely from the solid branch of an oak that has graced these lands for over one hundred years. We can see it. We can see just in the distance something that looks like an oversized pear . . . no, a bag, yes, a punch bag maybe as it sways ever so gently in the summer breeze.

She nears the tree, focused on maintaining her pace, focused on internal self-talk in order to stay motivated rather than lapse into a walk as she has done so many times before when out for a run. A line of lukewarm sweat trickles down past her sports bra and disappears somewhere in the lower part of her back.

She notices the man . . . a Black man with a small fluffy tan-coloured dog standing still. The man has a disturbed expression on his face. The dog is barking. It runs forward, barks and darts back to the man's side and continues barking. It repeats this four, five, six times maybe before it stops, pants for breath and once regained resumes the entire process.

She stops and, catching her breath, pulls out a headphone. The man turns to look at her and she then sees what has interrupted his walk.

There in the tree hangs a large cocoon-like object swaddled in a light paper-bag-brown material. She had heard something about these shapes before . . . seen in a number of parks and green spaces . . . but had not really paid them any attention. Apparently, some activist groups had been campaigning about them, but the exact issue had escaped her.

This one, though . . . she followed the man's gaze . . . this one was releasing a substance that looked very much like blood.

It was not meant to kill them.

The handheld technology was designed to immobilize the assailant for one minute and one minute only. The former

188

Home Secretary had been inspired, so it was said, by one of his ministers who, having returned from a trip to downtown Chicago, said that the Electronic Restrictive System (ERS) was revolutionizing crime reduction.[4]

What the minister had neglected to share was that the programme she had witnessed was still in pilot stage. She had also neglected (she would later be sacked) to share key documents setting out the risk factors and indeed the backlash, spearheaded by the NAACP, about the percentage of African American men who had ended up dead in the early days of the ERS pilots.[5] The Home Secretary had needed a win. He needed to show an otherwise demoralized police service that he was on their side. ERS provided that opportunity. So what that the pilot initially planned for Greater Manchester, West Midlands and the Met police forces had not yet been completed? He would sanction its rollout nationwide – after all, the police should be free to exercise their judgement about those tools that would best support their operational work.

The Electronic Restrictive System, once engaged, released a long rope (described in official documents as a 'temporary immobilizing device' since it was considered that this would make the ERS more palatable to potential critics) from a device held in the officer's hand. The rope was supposed to wrap itself around the arm or leg of the perpetrator and then stun them, but the system was faulty. Instead, it wrapped itself around their necks and, in some cases, stunned and restrained them for well over the minute indicated in the guidance materials authored by the technology experts.[6] And as the alleged assailant flailed and gasped and clawed in desperation at the rope, at the air, at anything, it became tighter.

189

It became tighter and tighter and, as it did so, it released layer upon layer of a thin cotton-like fabric that wound itself around and around the writhing, soon to be asphyxiated body: a beautiful artistic cocoon.

And so it came to pass that the bodies of the dead hung in trees across the nation, swaying back and forth, back and forth in the wind, for to return them to police stations or to hospitals would risk a disproportionate increase in the numbers of those killed in custody (known as death in custody data) and potential lambasting from the HMIC and the local PCC.[7]

Activists and human rights groups along with the parents and families of the dead had been campaigning and arguing for years that the Electronic Restrictive System was, in fact, a sophisticated modern form of lynching. They collated statistics. They shared heart-wrenching stories and the young amongst them posted recordings on social media of what a leading academic who specialized in police brutality called 'state-sanctioned slavery'. However, their calls for change were not heeded – until, that is, the cocoon on the heath incident.

Between them they agree that they will take it down, this swaying object that slowly weeps blood into the warm summer heat. She will record it on her phone and he will take it down. A tired-looking log serves as a step so he can stretch on tip toe up to the rope that adjoins the object to the tree. The fluffy tan-coloured dog is now whimpering as though he understands the mournful gravity of what is taking place.

The Black man almost keels over with the weight.

He starts to unwrap the swaddling.

He starts but is stopped dead in his tracks for he has never seen or heard about fabric like this before. This fabric is different. Tiny, sharp sheaths of jagged glass rise haphazardly from it and, on closer inspection, some of these are marked by the darkness of dried blood.

This is ERS mark II.

The Black boy who was its untimely victim was just seventeen years old.

It had slit his left cheek, his left earlobe, his head in several places and his throat.

Both runner and man are sickened to their core.

The runner posts the video on social media.

The press went crazy.

White people, stunned by this revelation of racism on their shores, rose as one to devour all that was Black. Books by every single Black author – both those about race and those which were not – were swept off shelves up and down the country.[8] Websites crashed such was the frenzy of white people to access them. Literary agents' phones rang off the hook and inboxes swelled as guilt and shock ravaged the nation. Never before (except roughly twenty years earlier when that Black boy was murdered in Eltham, southeast London, but we do not count him and nor do we count the racist murder of that other Black boy in Liverpool[9] or the one before that) had the nation witnessed such manic activity.

Any Black person who had put their name to a blog, Instagram account or had posted a single tweet about race during the previous month was hunted down and wheeled out to appear on news and debate programmes to be asked for their 'expert' analysis of what had happened. And, desperate for recognition in a country that had otherwise starved them of any presence, validity or visibility, those Black people gobbled up those calls. They gave their opinion and spoke as though they were the first to make such observations with no reference to historical context or to Elders who had been working in the field for decades before them. And white viewers and listeners drank it all in determined to satiate purportedly starved appetites.

The leading business publication *Del Momento*, not to be outdone by its rivals or indeed its own track record, published – in a journalistic first – the Top Ten under Ten (years of age) who were selected for their 'trailblazing work' on challenging racism. Entrants – most of whom were already known to journalists at the publication – had been selected for their 'thoughtful and inspiring' contributions such as having the fortitude to play with children from different neighbourhoods, building LEGO™ constructions that included key themes of 'diversity' and, a particularly moving piece, where a child had painted a self-portrait not in brown paint but in a pinky-white colour showing, the publication insisted, a 'refusal to be bound by the strictures of skin colour'. (In fact, the child's mother had been appalled that her brown-skinned child had not painted herself in her likeness and, having confronted the school, discovered that they only had 'neutral, skin tone' paints that did not include anything that matched little Jemima's. Such matters were listened to sympathetically and then summarily dismissed by the *Del Momento* editorial team: 'It really wouldn't fit with the narrative,' they said.)

The Ten were dressed in the latest Oscar de la Renta and during their first photoshoot were encouraged to take on sombre adult-like expressions that reflected the gravity of the 'awakening' that the country was experiencing. Turn left, turn right, it was impossible to avoid news coverage about The Ten, appearing as they did on morning and evening television and radio shows. One special child was invited to be guest editor of the *Today* programme for the slot during the quiet period between Christmas and New Year's Day and another – in a rapidly secured recording contract – released a sweet, pop version of 'I'm Dreaming of a White Christmas' just as the calendar switched from 30 November to 1 December.

The Ten became synonymous in the minds of guilty whites (and some emotionally weary and desperate Blacks) with hope, with the future, with the change that would surely come and release the country from the scourge of this very brutal phenomenon of racism. And to drive this home, the CEOs of the major advertising firms contacted the parents of the most attractive (they had now recognized that this did not just include the lighter-skinned ones with big hair) of The Ten to appear in a series of commercials during that season. Of course, racism mattered – that cocoon on the heath incident had been shocking and very upsetting – and while supporting this important cause there was also money to be made and money indeed would be made.

White people to the Far Right of the spectrum, and those whose politics sat in close proximity to them, took to social media to condemn this preoccupation with race. We are a country, they proclaimed aggressively, of individuals and those who did not like it should fuck off back where they came from. And lest you think these are a demographic to be ignored and merely tolerated: beware. For they count many a right-wing journalist – desperate to twist the innocent into the sensational – politician, actor and tired former presenter amongst their midst who collectively do a very good job of stirring up a crowd and convincing the 'undecided' that they should join their fast-growing cadre.

Time passes. Almost five years to be exact.

The country is licking its wounds from a race riot that apparently no one (aside from the Elders) had seen coming. The new Home Secretary described the smashing of shop windows and the looting that had unfolded as 'savage acts of criminality committed by a small but determined group of hoodlums and hooligans'. She reassured listeners, repeating it on every conceivable news channel, that 'no stone would be left unturned to root out the no-gooders from our midst' and that money (which had miraculously appeared from an unnamed budget) would be made available to support further prison reform programmes.

In this era almost five years after the cocoon on the heath incident, bodies no longer hang from trees, swaying ever so gently in the wind.

Instead, mysterious mounds of freshly dug earth – about the size of an average male body – begin to appear across the nation.

And no one hears the cries of growing numbers of Black mothers in Toxteth, in Handsworth, in Croydon and in downtown Chicago who start to report their sons missing.

———

Many years ago, during a period of spiritual soul-searching and curiosity, I attended an Alpha course. I met some warm and fascinating people from all walks of life. To my delight, asking questions of each other and the group leader was a central feature of the evangelical Christian programme. One of the many questions I posed was about the Church and the Transatlantic Slave Trade. While the Church had eventually been involved in the abolition of slavery it had initially, of course, been pivotal to enabling and sanctioning it. I wanted to know which present-day acts the Church might be sanctioning that in ten, twenty or a hundred years' time it might similarly reject and distance itself from. Our charismatic group leader received my question in good faith, started talking about William Wilberforce and neglected to answer it. My question was really a thought experiment designed to explore and test the rigour of our assumptions and values within different contexts. Ultimately, I am interested in how actions or principles that we adhere to doggedly today or in one context might, at another time, be regarded as offensive, outdated or regressive. This has served as the basis of this chapter about race and policing.

I examine the chilling extremes of the ways in which the treatment of Black males is rationalized and, in so doing, question how particular forms of control become sanctioned by the state and framed as acceptable. My provocation here is not whether regulation is necessary. Rather, I am asking who is in a position of power to authorize such decisions and how they go about the work of convincing others that their decisions are legitimate. The language used around such messaging is important, as is who is assigned responsibility for conveying the message. Statistical and other evidential material is also used, and if necessary reframed or used partially, to add authority and to defend courses of action even in the face of unpalatable or differential racial outcomes.

It is commonly said by those who do not need to make constant calculations about the surveillance being carried out on their bodies, that remaining within the bounds of legality should be sufficient to offer peace of mind.

However, such views require a subscription to what the philosopher Charles Mills describes as a 'racial fantasyland' that is based on a reading of the world through white eyes. It is only the white world that can be placated by the idea that innocence in this context brings with it ready liberation.

This chapter also highlights the performativity that characterizes white people's response to a horrific, high-profile, racist incident: the sudden desire to consume information about racism, the rush to demonstrate engagement with the issues. The Ten are an example of this but they also represent the way in which youth is fetishized by the media especially in mainstream debates about race and racism. This serves a purpose. A disproportionate focus on the young strips racism of historical context and continuity so that events are constantly presented as new as opposed to being contextualised alongside the voices and experiences of Elders and past racist incidents. It means that the activism and campaigning for racial justice as well as the indignities, suffering and triumphs that accompany it become dislodged from an overarching continuum and narrative of change. This racial amnesia benefits white people who have nothing to lose from this information vacuum but disadvantages Black people who constantly seek to prove the existence and salience of racism and its emotional consequences to whites.

The Persistence of the Racial Code

People of color, women, and gays – who now have greater access to the centers of influence than ever before – are under pressure to be well-behaved when talking about their struggles. There is an expectation that we can talk about sins but no one must be identified as a sinner: newspapers love to describe words or deeds as 'racially charged' even in those cases when it would be more honest to say 'racist'; we agree that there is rampant misogyny, but misogynists are nowhere to be found; homophobia is a problem, but no one is homophobic. One cumulative effect of this policed language is that when someone dares to point out something as obvious as white privilege, it is seen as unduly provocative.

Teju Cole (2012)

I wrote this book over the course of two years. For the most part, I squirrelled myself away in my study with books and papers stacked in perilous piles on the desk and the carpeted floor, overlooked by a handwritten chapter plan stuck to a wall with Blu Tack. This was the place I was permitted to lose myself in thoughts, words and ideas, to delete, rewrite and reorder sentences. However, on occasion, I sought escape from this enclave and took myself to a local pub garden to work in the company of strangers. One sunny afternoon, I was typing away diligently when a conversation from a neighbouring table drifted toward me. And although the occupants were obscured from my view by a trellised fence I could tell, partly because of the demography of the area and in part because of their accents, that they were probably mid- to late fifties, white and the solid, not afraid to speak their mind, made a bit of money, play golf at the weekend, type of working-class men. It was the day after England had failed to secure a goal in the Euro 2020 Final penalty shoot-out and the men's analysis segued from football to race.

'I get that this racism thing *does* happen. I really do,' said one. 'But the thing is, look at the prisons. There's more of 'em in there than us.'

I froze with what felt like a million internal conundrums wrestling around my mind.

Was this spoken at a volume I was meant to hear? No, that was clearly ridiculous. Should I, as a scholar specializing in racial justice, tell them what I knew and what the evidence said? Perhaps I should go over to them, introduce myself and tell them about the data on racial disproportionality in custodial sentences and how similar patterns are mirrored in school exclusions and even in police misconduct cases. But then, how might they react? No, interrupting them and their afternoon was a silly idea and yet . . . If I didn't intervene then they would leave the pub none the wiser. They would go back to families and friends and possibly even colleagues and spread those falsehoods amongst them. How could I let that happen? Didn't I have a responsibility to act and to be pro-active about my endeavours for racial justice? Then again, was it really my personal duty to take up the role of educa-tor? But how could I sit there as a Black woman with Black friends, nephews, cousins and allow them to parade non-sense? The questions swirled and I chastised myself for putting myself under such pressure; after all, I'd simply gone there to write. Surely, I was entitled to sit in a pub garden on a sunny day without feeling obligated to defend my Blackness . . . our Blackness? Besides, if I were to slide out of my seat and approach them, did I really expect them to welcome me with warm smiles, open arms and say, 'thanks very much, we didn't know that'?

And as these thoughts jostled with each other – my writing now abandoned – it occurred to me that I too had watched that same Euro Final between Italy and England. Like many others, I had perched on the edge of my seat, my heart pounding with trepidation, urging and praying that the players would get the ball into the back of the net. I hadn't even paid attention to the fact that most of the players in the shoot-out were Black. Others evidently had, for the following day, when I logged on to social media, I learnt that what I had anxiously borne witness to had, for some, become justification for racist vilification. I wondered what would have happened had we won but quickly recognized that this did not matter, for it was *the very readiness* to reach for skin colour that was the problem. In this case, it was attributed as supposed intrinsic justification of what went wrong and racist abuse ensued. It was this that had disturbed me about the conversation I overheard that day in the pub garden; the sense of being collectively demarcated by skin colour, of being pre-read, pre-judged without reflection or critique and of automatically being seen as a problem. Fanon's[1] sombre words about the Negro as seen through the eyes of the white man, returned to haunt me:

I am given no chance. I am overdetermined from without.

Breaking the First Rule

The counternarratives in this book reveal the casual, pervasive nature of everyday racism. They aim to lay bare the micro-calculations, the effort, the emotional cost and the fortitude required to navigate and survive in a society shaped by race and racism.

By invoking the concept of a code, I am suggesting that there is a structure or scaffold on to which we can map and identify the processes, behaviours and attitudes which keep racism in place. This scaffolding can help us better see the connections between what might appear to be isolated incidents but which, in reality, are deeply rooted and historically intertwined. It offers a useful analogy to envisage the commonalities between the assumptions and behaviours white people hold and enact about race which they otherwise endeavour to present as individual deliberations. I hope this book will be useful to those who are keen to understand what it means to possess and exercise white privilege and power and, by engaging honestly with the questions set out here, they will be able to start to recognize the characteristics of white allyship and anti-racist practice. Such work will necessarily be uncomfortable because it means embracing an examination of the world from a new position, in other words from a critical understanding of what it means to be racialized as white. It means moving past defensiveness and denial and the presumption of *de facto* greater knowledge in this subject area and moving toward humility, active listening and some element of responsibility for one's actions and for change. I hope, too, that with its unique foregrounding of everyday accounts of racism backed by links to sources of

evidence and analysis, this book will also serve as an affirm-
ing point of reference for people of colour and help us move
beyond the second-guessing that is an understandable consequence of being subjected to sense-defying acts of racism.[2]

The word 'code' also implies secrecy and the protection
of privileged information to which few have access. This is
befitting because, in part, racism retains its momentum precisely because it is fluid and because of efforts to deny,
downplay and ignore its complexity and pervasiveness.[3] It is
a trauma about which people of colour are not permitted to
speak publicly. The tendency of those racialized as white –
and their racially minoritized collaborators – to direct the
narrative on race and racism is an exercise, or more accurately *an abuse*, of power. Racism becomes what white people
want it to be, what they are willing to concede and what they
can tolerate. And they are seldom willing to concede the significance of their part in enabling it, for that would require a
drastic shift in their self-image and to the status quo. By
exposing the systemic nature of everyday racism and by
making explicit the role of white people in maintaining it, I
am breaking one of *the* foundational principles of the racial
code: I am both naming the problem and, to borrow from
Teju Cole, identifying the 'sinner'.

There are, of course, consequences to flouting the rules in
this way, and it is worth considering some of the accusations
likely to be levelled at the book (and indeed at me) for daring
to give voice to these realities.

You always make it about race

The accusation 'you always make it about race' is typically
made by those who claim not to see colour and want to

downplay its significance or want to deploy it as and when *they* deem appropriate.[4] It is to overlook the substantial body of empirical research carried out by academics from across a range of disciplines and by policymakers examining different areas of policy which continues to highlight evidence of persistent unexplained racial disparities. It is to relegate as insignificant the grassroots determinations of activists, campaigners and families (the latter often as a result of personal tragedy) in exposing precisely how racism has consistently shaped the poorer outcomes for and treatment of racially minoritized communities.

For these *race deniers*, merely mentioning race even as a descriptor is met with disproval and mislabelled as being racist. Therefore, to dare go one step further and discuss race *and* racism is to provoke discomfort, anger and denial. It is to introduce discord and disrupt a version of reality that is comfortably predicated on a white worldview and self-image. In such situations, those naming racism become remade into the problem. Irrespective of their standing or expertise, they are accused of *having a chip on their shoulder*, of *special pleading*, of *always making it about race* and of *causing division*. Such counterarguments lack substance and rigour because they imply that there must be some benefit to conjuring up accounts of racism and declaring it a factor in shaping the experiences of racially minoritized communities.

Putting racism momentarily to one side, there is, at a fundamental interpersonal level, something inherently problematic and unhealthy in a dynamic in which one party steadfastly refuses to acknowledge the pain they have caused another, preferring instead to promulgate a stance of defensiveness and increased criticism against the complainant. This pattern of behaviour resonates with the literature on narcissistic abuse where the needs and interests of the narcissist are consistently prioritized ahead of others. In the context of the racial code, it is the perspectives and needs of those racialized as white which continue to be re-centred.[5]

Believing in racism makes you lazy

This is a close bedfellow of *you always make it about race*. Advocates of this perspective claim that merely discussing race and encouraging debate about experiences of racism is sufficient to incite despondency, fecklessness and general lack of ambition amongst people of colour. It is a patronizing viewpoint because it renders people of colour as lacking the maturity to cope with the fact that racial disadvantage exists and, moreover, implies that they do not possess the agency and fortitude to challenge or navigate it. It is also manipulative in that it serves to neatly redirect any lack of progress or success back on to racially minoritized groups themselves. In this way, they become responsible for their own downfall.

Claiming that a belief in or experience of racism makes you lazy also undermines decades of activism that have seen racially minoritized communities establish political movements, fight for their rights, set up initiatives, projects and schemes in deliberate, proactive efforts to overcome racism and empower their own communities, and it downplays the achievements that they *have* made despite encountering racism.

It's racist to call white people white

Speaking candidly about racism is fraught with risk for people of colour because it means pointing out and critiquing the behaviours and attitudes of those racialized as white. As we saw in *Members Only*, this is further complicated by the fact that white people tend to resist categorization as white or that they are implicated in perpetuating racism. In his essay *Between the World and Me*, Ta-Nehisi Coates posits that 'those who believe themselves to be white are obsessed with the politics of personal exoneration'.[6] Adopting this standpoint is beneficial for white people because it aligns with a narrative of individualism therefore absolving them from taking collective responsibility for their part in constructing and maintaining racism even while they continue to be advantaged by it. It is an especially subversive form of denial because it rejects the necessary foundational variable – that they are a racialized group – that would permit any further examination of the racism problem.[7] Consequently, any argument predicated on the premise of *group* assumptions or *group* behaviours can be readily dismissed and the idea that they, as a group, hold power can be rejected. Instead, white people become unique, differentiated individuals and their whiteness an incidental irrelevance to their existence.

You hate white people

At various moments throughout this book, I have used the phrase *racialized as white*.[8] Critical scholars of race argue that this terminology helps establish a distinction between skin colour and the learnt behaviours and attitudes which constitute whiteness.[9] Put very simply, the problem is not that white people are bad or indeed hated but that they have uncritically learnt and adopted assumptions and behaviours which prioritize their interests while being oppressive to people of colour. It is this that is being challenged.

A consistent argument throughout this book is that those who form part of any dominant group design the rules and benefit from others executing and adhering to them. This is an enactment of power. Anti-racists, like feminists, challenge the power held by their corresponding dominant group and advocate for a more equitable future. By and large, debates surrounding feminism and women's equality are sufficiently advanced that it is understood that supporting this agenda does not by default equate to hating men. It does, however, necessitate examination of how men operate through processes of patriarchy to oppress women and mete out differential treatment. This same equation ought to hold true for those striving to advance racial justice. However, because those racialized as white tend to refute the idea that they *are* white, the debate seldom moves on to the next pivotal stage, which is the recognition that they hold power relative to racially minoritized populations and the ways in which this is oppressive and can be challenged.

Through this lens, it becomes easier to understand why feminist arguments and debates about (cis) women's equality have gained some degree of traction relative to anti-racist ones. Their debate is not fixated on circular arguments about whether men are indeed men and whether men hold collective power. By contrast, anti-racists become regarded not as advocates for racial equity determined to help create a level playing field amongst differing racialized groups but rather as inventing problems where there are none, being divisive and as hating white people.[10]

It's really about social class

This charge implies that class-based advantages such as maternal education, qualifications, attending the so-called right school and university, income and occupation outstrip inequalities of race. To my mind this is predicated on a reductive interpretation of racism which ignores the complex ways in which it operates and is *differentially* inflected by class. To be clear, middle-class status can help mitigate racism in a way that being working class cannot, but middle-class status alone does not guarantee protection from racism. Black men do not avoid being stopped and searched simply because they are middle class.

There is a second point to be made about the matter of class which relates to fundamental assumptions about the production of knowledge and power. When white people counter that 'it's really about social class' – and it is a common refrain – it implies that people of colour have not considered this themselves and that they are seeking, without due thought, to affix *any* disadvantage or problem to race. Yet, it is precisely because 'it's really about social class' is uttered so frequently that we must consider why and the purpose it serves. It indicates a refusal to accept racism as real or as presented while simultaneously imposing, and presuming more viable, a reading of the world from a white lens. In so doing, the assertion that 'it's really about social class' masquerades as an intellectually palatable form of gaslighting rendering invisible the racism experienced by middle-class people of colour while also undermining their analytical and interpretative capabilities.

Not all white people are the same

Some white people will readily recognize the matters described in this book and comprehend the challenge such issues present. Such white people are likely to recognize themselves as racialized as white and endeavour to be pro-active in their efforts to address racial injustice. When it comes to discussions about race and racism involving people of colour, they strive to embrace humility (even when offer-ing challenge), to actively listen as opposed to asserting their knowledge and worldview as superior and are open to learn-ing and understanding what they do not know. Such individuals are likely to be described as allies and as growing in their racial maturity.

However, those who are earlier on in their journey tend to enter debates about racism as though they are equally or more knowledgeable as those subjected to or experts in it. As we witnessed with Sally in *Nigel's Story*, they determine that certain personal experiences such as class disadvantage, hav-ing mixed-race family members or knowing a single Black person with whom they talk about race can be regarded as sufficient qualifiers of their expertise. Such experiences are uncritically generalized to serve as the evidential basis for their arguments about racism. White people at this end of the continuum display a *restrictive racial worldview*, character-ized by defensiveness, denial and a lack of self-reflection where there is scope only for their perspective and where opportunity for growth is limited. By acting in this way, they reinforce the tenets of whiteness and prioritize and privilege white needs over an understanding that is racially inclusive.

What White People Really Know about Race

I have been keen, throughout this book, to draw attention to the strategic ways people of colour work to navigate racism and how those racialized as white enable it. This is important since, despite continued declarations and commitments to advancing racial justice, we still find ourselves debating whether racism (particularly anti-Black racism) is real and whether it plays a role in shaping the experiences of and outcomes for racially minoritized groups. Obviously, we must ask why this continues to be the case and, as an essential part of this, seek to identify the barriers to enabling change and establish what success looks like. The second part of this equation ought to be relatively straightforward: my child should have similar opportunities for success to his white middle-class counterpart so that there are fewer racial disparities in their eventual achievements. However, for this to be truly meaningful, it necessitates an acknowledgement that even if their starting points are roughly equivalent, racism will likely impede my child's progress. This should mean that interventions are put in place to reduce or ideally eliminate the barriers that he is likely to experience en route.

The first part of the equation deserves closer scrutiny. If we take institutional commitments promising change seriously, then we must explore the impediments to progress and, moreover, why it is not occurring at a pace which is agreeable to people of colour. Central to our considerations is that there is an unevenness in terms of who holds prevailing power and who is able to exercise it. White people tend to have access to networks of influence and have the financial resources and the status to sanction projects, appointments and so on aimed at changing the landscape on racial justice. These resources, and the ability to make use of them, are examples of power. Yet, recall my earlier argument that white people are not impacted if existing racial inequalities remain the same and, in fact, benefit from maintaining the status quo because it means they do not need to radically change their behaviour or engage in a redistribution of power. As such, given the slow pace of progress, we should be compelled to reassess the extent to which white people *are* invested in change and really are neutral or oblivious to the complexities of racism given that they operationalize rules which continue to work in their favour.[11] With this in mind, I set out some of the ways in which white people seek to demonstrate their commitment to advancing racial justice while, in fact, holding steadfast to existing practices:

A white person's guide to preserving racism in the modern age

1 Appoint unqualified white people to lead work on anti-racism.

2 Pretend not to notice or avoid identifying incidents of racism.

3 Don't speak up when white peers are undermining people of colour but . . .

4 . . . assume greater knowledge of race and racism than people of colour.

5 Grant yourself the authority to grade your own racial awareness and competence.

6 Situate your assessment of your racial knowledge as superior to that of people of colour (including experts in the field). Ideally, back up your arguments by citing a few books by people of colour or get rid of the experts altogether.

7 Silence and gaslight people of colour.

8 Dismiss and take offence at being labelled 'white'. You are an individual.

9 Only notice race when it pertains to racially minoritized groups.

10 Become defensive when conversation turns to race. Good strategies include:

- Not allowing the person of colour to finish their point
- Insisting that language such as 'racism' is offensive and hurtful[12]
- Stating that their point is anecdotal and therefore without merit
- Insist there are alternative interpretations of what is being said (the person of colour won't have considered these themselves).

11 Wholeheartedly support initiatives that will not impact on structural change or drastically change mindsets.

12 Take up the role of race champion or sponsor especially if you've done no work looking at your own whiteness.

13 In contentious workplace situations involving employees of colour, protect yourself and the organization at ALL costs even if it flagrantly undermines stated institutional commitment to racial justice and irrespective of the likely impact on the employee.

14 Look the other way when employees of colour leave the organization. We operate in a global economy after all.

15 Counter any initiative or project about race by saying either: 'what about white people? All lives matter' or 'we must prioritize excellence'.

16 If you find yourself in a situation where one of them says they are insulted by some racial microaggression or the other, either deny that it was offensive or, if so compelled, show your disregard for the situation by saying '*If* you are offended, then I apologize'. Under no circumstances offer a sincere apology or acknowledgement of their pain for it legitimizes their experiences and existence and heavens knows where that will lead.

17 It never hurts to mentor one or two of them. This can be
    useful evidence of racial goodwill if a charge of racism is
    brought against you at some point in the future.

18 If a complaint is made about something you said which is
    clearly racist, counter by insisting your freedom of speech
    is being curtailed and that freedom of speech is the
    bedrock of democracy.

The Emperor's New Clothes

Institutions use differing benchmarks to insist that they are
making progress in eliminating racism and in increasing
opportunities for racially minoritized groups. One common
approach involves comparing current behaviours and trends
with past patterns or failings. This, of course, makes sense if
informed by a valid and reasonable interpretation of the
data. For example, the increasing number of interracial relationships and the ensuing fast-growing pace of the population
within the ethnically 'mixed' category is true. However, this
is often cited as a sign of racial progress, an analysis which is
predicated on a fundamentally problematic premise. It infers
that the only way in which I, as a Black woman, will see
change is if I elect to date outside of my racial group. My
argument here is not about my personal or individual preferences *per se*; rather that racial advancement is presented as
possible *only if* I reject building a family with someone who
looks like me and invest in the idea of a mixed-heritage family. The argument does not hold the other way around, say,
for my hypothetical white partner because white people
occupy a place of racial advantage, a status that is not changed
because of who they partner with.

Sometimes organizations endeavour to give the *impression* that their track record is improving. In such contexts, racial progress becomes a performative act; that is, an arena in which the institution must be *seen* to be making strides even if the data and the experiences of their racially minoritized employees indicate otherwise. A typical approach to such reframing involves identifying mediocre or low baselines for comparison and positioning these against the otherwise pitiful advances of their own organization. In this way, the organization becomes remade as progressive and outstanding.[13] To define success in this way establishes a low standard for change, encourages society and people of colour themselves to be placated by falsehoods and prioritizes image and brand over honesty and critical self-examination. If we are to move the dial on racial justice, bold, honest leadership and ownership of institutional failings is essential and central to building trust amongst racially minoritized groups themselves.

Central to this entire debate is that those racialized as white and racially minoritized groups have entirely different understandings, relationships and investments in racism, therefore, as Ladson-Billings[14] reminds us, their respective benchmarks for progression and success are unlikely to match: '[. . .] liberal approaches to race relations presume steady progress toward racial equality. What is not included in the narrative are the deliberate, intentional ways inequitable structures have been planned to ensure that race would be a permanent dividing line between Whites and those not designated as White.'

When reflecting on this subject, I often wonder whether those white people who offer reassurance to people of colour that progress is being made would accept the same measures and the same glacial rates of change if it concerned their own life chances and those of their families and friends. 'Progress' and 'change' are the words of those who do not fully comprehend the extent of the problem or are not impacted by it.

I was in the process of writing this book when George Floyd was murdered. I was struck by how many white people described having been jolted into a state of 'awakening' by what happened. It was as though they were bearing witness to the horrors of racism for the first time. It is as though they choose to be oblivious to the everyday traumas and inequalities of race foisted upon them by reports, by inquiries and via data from their own institutions.

White people can afford not to be awake. They can choose not to see. They can close their ears.

Such luxuries are not available to people of colour.

Hope and the idea that progress is being made are closely aligned. They both rest on shallow interpretations of the race problem. However, racially minoritized communities and those fighting for racial justice understand that hope can be deployed as a placating device while substantive reform remains out of reach, or the goalposts are moved.[15] I am not saying that being hopeful is futile. We must have hope. But it must be grounded in a serious analysis of how we make sense of and hold onto the realities of racism. And this must include an understanding of its persistent nature and above all, a willingness to acknowledge and live beyond the principles of the racial code.

Endnotes

Introduction

1 In the preface of her book *Feminist Theory: From Margin to Center*, the African American scholar bell hooks describes the margins as 'part of the whole but outside the main body' (p.ix) where the main body refers to mainstream society, its culture and norms. She goes on to argue in *Yearning: Race, Gender and Cultural Politics* that occupying the space in the margins can offer one 'the possibility of radical perspectives from which to see and create, to imagine alternative, new worlds' (bell, 1990: 150). It is necessary to learn how to survive and exist in the margins *and* negotiate an existence within the mainstream.

2 Mandela, 1993, cited in Lawrence (2006) in which Doreen Lawrence details her family's experiences of her son's murder.

3 Tom Cook (a retired Deputy Chief Constable for West Yorkshire), The Right Reverend Dr John Sentamu (Bishop of Stepney) and Dr Richard Stone (a former GP and chair of the Jewish Council for Racial Equality).

4 The term in fact has its origins in the 1960 works of Stokely Carmichael and Charles Hamilton. They argued that institutional racism 'is less overt, far more subtle, less identifiable in terms of *specific* individuals committing the acts. But it is no less destructive of human life. [It] originates in the operation of established and respected forces in the society, and thus receives far less public condemnation' (Carmichael and Hamilton, 1967, original emphasis, cited in Cashmore & Jennings, 2001: 112).

5 Section 95 is a part of the Criminal Justice Act 1991. Published by the Ministry of Justice, Section 95 data captures statistics about different ethnic groups and the criminal justice system across England and Wales.

6 The government at the time fast-tracked changes to the Race Relations Act in order to introduce what became known as the Race
Relations (Amendment) Act 2000.

7 The targets were put in place in 1999 with a ten-year deadline. Writing in 2008, the then Home Secretary Jacqui Smith commented:

> For several years, the Home Office and agencies have met the rep-
> resentation targets set in respect of race. However, the Police
> Service continue to attract media attention in respect of their
> minority ethnic representation and how police forces are driving
> race equality. It is encouraging that 20 out of the 43 police forces
> have now met their race targets. A further 5 forces are within reach
> of meeting their targets. (Home Office, 2008)

For a wider discussion, see Rollock, N. (2009) *The Stephen Lawrence
Inquiry 10 Years On.*

8 The term 'sus' or 'sus laws' derives from Section 4 of the 1824
Vagrancy Act which gave police officers the power to stop anyone
they suspected of loitering with intent to commit an arrestable
offence. Campaigning organizations such as the West Indian
Standing Committee and the Scrap Sus Campaign drew attention
to the way in which the procedure was deployed disproportionately, inappropriately and often aggressively against young Black
men. The procedure was ultimately scrapped in 1981. For further
discussion see Rollock, N. (2009) *The Stephen Lawrence Inquiry 10
Years On.*

9 BBC News (2009) 'Met is "no longer racist" – Straw', Sunday 22
February.

10 The two-year study, funded by the Society for Educational Studies,
examined how race had been interpreted and incorporated within
education policy. Speaking to me in 2015 as part of that project,
Straw commented:

> I did feel compared with the situation we had before that we had
> made significant gains, [. . .] I'm pretty certain I would have cave-
> ated it by saying that it's difficult for me to judge this because I'm
> a white bloke. But my sense is, and also what people from the
> Black and Asian community report is that [. . .] there is a view that

progress has been made, and [. . .] Black people and Asian people are treated with significantly more respect [. . .] not only when I was a youngster but also 15, 20 years ago. So that's what I meant, but I certainly don't think that we've reached in any sense a state of grace [. . .]

11 Personal notes; Dodd (2009).
12 In his speech written to mark the tenth anniversary of the Lawrence Inquiry report, Phillips (2009) explained:

> Let me be clear, I am not saying that institutional racism as it was described in the Stephen Lawrence Inquiry report has been obliterated. Public institutions are not now exonerated with a single sweep. Our mission has not been achieved.
>
> But we need to stop rerunning the same old argument as though nothing had [*sic*] changed. That is because we have actually succeeded in gaining much change, partly through the work of those who campaigned with the Lawrence family; and because we now know that we face a new challenge that needs new methods and new remedies.
>
> If we need to give that challenge a name let's call it, for example, systemic bias – the way in which the system works to destroy our ambition for fairness and our desire for equality; and the way it can disadvantage people because of their race, gender, sexuality, age or disability – or indeed their class – in spite of everyone's efforts to the contrary.

13 I am particularly indebted to scholars who have led the way in this field including bell hooks, Derrick Bell and Charles Mills whose writings provide the intellectual and creative backdrop for this book.
14 Akala (2018) offers an accessible and engaging overview of these historical processes, teasing out the tensions and overlaps between class and racial inequalities.
15 See Chapter 8, *A Special Kind of Madness* and *The Persistence of the Racial Code*.
16 Sometimes people of colour are deployed as Trojan Horses to do this same work. Such individuals are useful to white people because they speak the same language and espouse similar ideas about race and

racism. My argument is not that all racially minoritized groups *should* hold exactly the same views about race; rather, as we shall see in the chapters which follow, it is the ways in which they are celebrated and utilized by their white peers that is of interest.

17 Of course, I recognize the racisms experienced by particular white groups, for example Jews, Gypsies, Roma and Traveller communities. This book is primarily interested in anti-Black racism.

18 The author, poet and academic Claudia Rankine has argued instead for the term 'white living' in order to avoid the common miscomprehension (mostly among white people) that white privilege refers to wealth acquisition, to draw attention to the normalcy of whiteness in everyday life and the ability of whites to navigate society relatively unmarked by the colour of their skin. While I recognize this ongoing misinterpretation of the phrase, in my view, 'white living' underplays the ways in which white people are advantaged as a consequence of their racialized identity. I also believe we need to exercise vigilance about the way in which certain phrases continue to be misread, leaving racially minoritized groups in a perpetual state of explanation and reclarification (also see Morrison, 1975).

19 There is no scientific evidence indicating a *biological difference* between those principal groups of differing skin colour. This fact was confirmed in the 1950 UNESCO statement on race, agreed by the world's leading anthropologists, geneticists, sociologists and psychologists:

> The biological fact of race and the myth of 'race' should be distinguished. For all practical social purposes 'race' is not so much a biological phenomenon as a social myth. The myth of 'race' has created an enormous amount of human and social damage. [. . .] it has taken a heavy toll in human lives and caused untold suffering.

This myth operates *as though* biological differences are real. And it is this myth and the ways in which it operates that I draw attention to in this book.

20 The legal scholar Richard Delgado (2000: 60) explains that this form of writing is important in the context of understanding and challenging the status quo by inviting us to engage in realities that extend beyond the mainstream:

The dominant group creates its own stories [. . .] The stories or narratives told by the ingroup remind it of its identity in relation to outgroups, and provide it with a form of shared reality in which its own superior position is seen as natural.

The stories of outgroups aim to subvert that reality.

21 Speaking in Parliament during Black History Month 2020, the Black Conservative MP Kemi Badenoch (incorrectly) condemned Critical Race Theory as representing 'a dangerous trend in race relations [. . .] [and] an ideology that sees my blackness as victimhood and their whiteness as oppression'. She went on to state that the government was unequivocally opposed to CRT and to its teaching within schools (Badenoch, 2020). At the time, Badenoch was the Minister for Equalities. Her stance follows a widespread backlash against CRT in the US where some states have sought to introduce legislation banning its teaching in schools and any arguments that uphold the idea of racism and sexism. For a useful, comprehensive overview of the US situation, see Sawchuk (2021) and the related map and table setting out actions taken at state level (*Education Week*, 2021).

22 See, in particular, the work of Bell (1992); Crenshaw, Gotanda, Peller & Thomas (1996); Delgado & Stefancic (2001); Ladson-Billings (1998); Tate (1997).

23 For a brief, accessible overview of Critical Race Theory, including its central arguments and suggestions for further reading, see Rollock & Gillborn (2011).

24 Crucially, scholars who make use of CRT do not simply see race everywhere. It is not a default position that automatically eradicates the possibility of other or additional explanations. However, they do acknowledge the likelihood of its existence in shaping experiences and outcomes.

25 The tradition when writing counternarrative is to use footnotes rather than endnotes but the layout of the book has been tailored for a broader non-academic audience.

26 Given that I am not drawing on any single individual but a composite of research and different experiences, identifying with the characters or some aspect of their behaviour ought to serve as a useful reflection of the ways in which we are racialized.

A Brief Note on Terminology

1 Racialization – the process of becoming racialized – has been described at length by scholars and writers interested in examining the dynamics of race (for example, see Hall, 1995; Sivanandan, 2000). From a more popular perspective, Chimamanda Ngozi Adichie's character Ifemelu speaks to this same process in her novel *Americanah* (2013: 290) when she says: 'I came from a country where race was not an issue; I did not think of myself as black and I only became black when I came to America.'

1: Acts of a Lone Woman

1 Decolonization refers to actions aimed at challenging and subverting colonization in order to give space to and include the experiences of racially marginalized groups. While there have been a number of efforts to make the higher education sector more racially inclusive, the Rhodes Must Fall campaign initiated at the University of Cape Town in 2015 is widely seen as the pivotal moment in bringing decolonization efforts to a wider platform. The campaign spurred widespread activity across several universities in the US and in the UK including the 'I too am . . .' campaign and initiatives aimed at interrogating 'Why is my professor not Black?' and 'Why is my curriculum white?'

However, anti-racist scholars and activists argue that universities (i.e. management and academics) have misinterpreted calls for decolonization by foregrounding superficial acts such as including the names of one or two people of colour in reading lists or, as in this chapter, changing the name of buildings. True decolonization requires a radical overhaul of not just the curriculum or building names but also who is teaching and how, and how power is distributed. For further reading see: Bhambra, Gebrial & Nisancioglu (2018); Chaudhuri (2016).

2 Conventionally, the academic career path, in the UK, runs: Lecturer, Senior Lecturer, Reader, Professor, although it is increasingly common for universities to mirror the US route of Assistant, Associate, Full Professor. Proportionally, Black women are least likely to reach

the most senior academic position of Professor compared with Black men, white women and white men (Rollock, 2019).

3 For useful debates about the controversies surrounding the use of this acronym see Fakim & Macaulay (2020); Bunglawala (2019).

4 See Leathwood, Maylor & Moreau (2009).

5 Bhopal, Brown & Jackson (2015).

6 It matters that Femi is at an elite university. In the UK higher education sector, there are fewer scholars of colour at elite Russell Group institutions. Her very presence, therefore, in such a space represents an anomaly. She has done well to get there.

7 This was the conclusion of the first nationwide study into the educational experiences of Black middle-class families. While the Black middle-class families we spoke to had cultural and social capital in the form, for example, of knowledge about the education system and access to tutors, their ability to make full use of these resources was curtailed by white gatekeepers. We therefore argued that race does not trump middle-class status. See Rollock, Vincent, Gillborn & Ball (2014).

8 Published in 2014 by the government's Social Mobility and Child Poverty Commission, the report *Elitist Britain?* highlighted a culture of elitism so pronounced that, in the words of the Commission's Chairman, it could be called 'social engineering'.

9 Smith (2004: 180) talks of the 'chronic race-related stressors' that people of colour experience as a result of racism. These include tension headaches and backaches, trembling and jumpiness, rapid breathing in anticipation of conflict, upset stomach, extreme fatigue and increased anxiety and broken sleep.

10 Similar experiences are reported by Black female professors for the first major UK research study examining their careers and strategies. The women described an uneven promotions process that lacked transparency and where feedback on unsuccessful applications was scant (Rollock, 2019a).

11 See Rollock (2021).

12 See research by University & College Union (2012) which shows the underrepresentation of women and Black and minority ethnic professors even after having taken account of their number in lower academic grades.

13 Source: Rollock (2019a).

2: The Meeting

1   Debates about Black hair have proliferated in recent years with back-lash against mainstream practices that negate afro textures and styles (Weekes-Barnard, 1997; Sini, 2016). For further exploration of this topic, see Chapter 6, *V.O.Y.E.U.R.*

2   The underrepresentation of Black and minority ethnic groups at senior levels of organizations has been a long-standing issue. Writing in 2010 for the Runnymede Trust, Veena Vasista identified a phenom-enon she described as 'snowy peaks' to reflect the disproportionate number of white employees at these levels compared with those from racially minoritized groups. Significantly, she noted: 'in many companies equal opportunities policies are not translating into cultur-ally different workplaces that feel fair and inclusive at all levels' (2010: 9). Progress in this area remains slow. In 2017, the McGregor-Smith review reported that Black and minority ethnic groups remain both underemployed and underpromoted within the workforce.

3   Though the name is a reference to the ancient city that was once part of Mesopotamia, the term Babylon is commonly used by Rastafarians – and borrowed by Black people outside of the religion – to refer, in shorthand, to the dominant order or oppressive systems of power (Kebede & Knottnerus, 1998).

4   The McGregor-Smith review (2017) documented that Black and minor-ity employees are less likely to apply for and be given promotions:

> BME individuals also struggle to achieve the same progression opportunities as their White counterparts. One in eight of the working age population are from a BME background, yet only one in ten are in the workplace and only one in 16 top manage-ment positions are held by an ethnic minority person. In terms of opportunities for progression 35% of Pakistani, 33% of Indian and 29% of Black Caribbean employees report feeling that they have been overlooked for promotion because of their ethnicity.

5   In his excellent satire about race, Nels Abbey describes HR as 'the most despised group in corporate life' (2019: 38).

6 The term 'gaslighting' derives from a 1944 film starring Ingrid Bergman and Charles Boyer in which the latter engages in a series of psychological tactics to confuse and distort Bergman's reality in favour of his own. The term continues to be used as shorthand for manipulative, abusive behaviours aimed at destabilizing and distressing its subjects. These acts take on a particular toxicity when abusers make use of macro-level inequalities to subjugate their victims (see Sweet, 2019).

7 Often referred to as 'white saviour complex' (Bandyopadhyay, 2019; Hinsliff, 2019), its historical basis stems from colonialism and the presumption of white traders and missionaries that indigenous peoples were inferior to whites and needed saving from their 'savage' ways and ungodly traditions. The term continues to be pertinent in situations where whites position themselves as the ones who can redeem, forgive or otherwise save usually economically disadvantaged minoritized people who are not deemed capable of exercising agency themselves. Although the term has been in circulation for some time, it gained widespread traction in the UK in 2019 following the MP David Lammy's criticism that the charity Comic Relief was uncritically making use of white celebrities to portray all Africans in a bad light in order to advance their cause (Lammy, 2017; Bell, 2013).

8 See Lacy (2007) for an excellent discussion of this point about attire and public identities that middle-class Black Americans deliberately consider to navigate mainly white spaces.

9 The names of these HR women draw on existing tropes which speak to the ways white women (see Chapter 6, *V.O.Y.E.U.R.*) who occupy these roles enact particular forms of behaviour to regulate and control staff in order to protect the organization. 'Karen' draws on a particular caricature of white female privilege which regards any person of colour as a threat and will go to extreme lengths to protect herself as a result:

> It is taken as read that her complaint is bogus, or at least disproportionate to the vigor with which she pursues it. The target of Karen's entitled anger is typically presumed to be a racial minority or a working-class person, and so she is executing a covert manoeuvre: using her white femininity to present herself as a victim, when she is really the aggressor. (Lewis, 2020)

Amy Cooper, the white woman who in 2020 falsely accused the African American birdwatcher Christian Cooper of threatening her, is an example of a Karen.

'Sally in HR' is a character developed by the actress, podcaster and fitness instructor Kelechi Okafor. Speaking to Circle Around™ (an online digital platform aimed at supporting women), Okafor explained her thinking behind the concept:

> I think HR gets a bad rap because they are essentially the gate-keepers. When we talk about, 'Oh, there's a lack of diversity in these companies,' they are the people that could essentially make a change. They can make that change regardless of how draconian or archaic the views of the CEO might be, and all of these other people that we see in the higher echelons of business. The HR people still have a chance to justify why they're bringing in new people, different people, yet they don't. They stick to the status quo. They bring in the same people all of the time. And yet, they'll put on their sites, their websites, 'Oh, we care about diversity. We care about inclusion,' yet all of the smiling faces are white and predominantly male. It's worrying. And that's the reason why, because they are kind of responsible for the well-being of the staff in terms of bringing them in and making sure the environment is one that's conducive for them working there. Yet, they fall so short of it constantly. After your interview, you don't really interact with them unless there's a complaint, and you don't want that. [. . .] HR has the reputation that it has because the people who end up in these roles are so happy to just have people who look like themselves come through. (Harts, 2019)

10 Such self-help books tend to focus on the individual and what they can do to navigate their institution. This is important but I am especially interested in the tension between individual strategies and the pervasive cultural norms and expectations of the workplace.

11 A large-scale survey by Business in the Community of over 24,000 Black and minority ethnic employees found that despite greater ambitions for progression and success, Black and minority ethnic people continue to experience racial harassment and do not feel valued at work (BiTC, 2015).

12 This was one of the conclusions of research carried out by the race equality think tank the Runnymede Trust into representation in senior positions:

> Many organizations considered leaders in promoting diversity still struggle to see talent rise to the top positions. The issue is that process-focused activities to diversify entry-level recruitment e.g. scrutinizing job specifications for potential indirect discrimination or advertising more widely are not impacting on the behaviours that disadvantage individuals in their career progression. Leaders in big business thought that bringing in more diverse recruits at entry level would automatically result in culture change and greater diversity at the top. They acknowledge, however, that this has not happened. (Vasista, 2010: 9)

13 NDAs have received increased scrutiny following the #MeToo movement (Barmes, 2022). While their use, in some cases, may offer protection to the employee as well as the employer, there are concerns that they are sometimes used as a mechanism to cover up unlawful discrimination and harassment. That is, their use may sometimes be unlawful and mask organizational problems rather than enabling scrutiny, growth and accountability:

> [...] the misuse of NDAs is one element of a wider system of legislative, regulatory and judicial measures and processes that are failing to protect employees from discrimination and abuse of power. Individuals who have experienced discrimination can feel that they have no option but to reach a settlement, which will routinely include secrecy clauses. We have seen that the use of unethical, vague or excessively restrictive NDAs can create long-lasting fear for those who sign them and can curtail their career. (Women and Equalities Committee, 2019)

As such, NDAs and how and when they are deployed also act as a yardstick for assessing the organization's cultural competence and maturity regarding its management of employees and the handling of complaints and grievances.

Interlude: *How Many Times?*

1 Written and performed for the 2018 Women of the World festival at London's Southbank Centre. The session was called 'Code switching: how women of colour survive in the workplace'.

2 These arguments were particularly popular in the early 2000s, for example Lightfoot (2000); Richardson (2011).

3 The refusal to see race when it pertains to white people means that debates about women, by default, tend to focus on white women. Little if any attention is paid to the fact of their whiteness or how being white means their experiences might intersect with but be different to those of women of colour. Joseph Harker (2017) makes this point in relation to debates about the gender pay gap at the BBC. For academic arguments about intersectionality see Crenshaw (1989; 1991).

4 My research on the career experiences of Black female professors showed that white women as well as white men were reported to undermine and bully Black women (Rollock, 2019a).

5 White, privately educated men are overrepresented in leading those institutions that have the most influence on what happens in the UK. I have written about this disproportionality in relation to higher education (see Rollock, 2019b). Also see Gary Younge's (2018) incisive article which speaks to the different life chances and opportunities afforded to white men compared with Black women.

6 Former US President Barack Obama used this refrain in the run up to his presidential election in 2008. It subsequently became closely associated with his values and politics. See Mieder (2009).

3: *Members Only*

1 Though people tend to use 'positive discrimination' and 'positive action' interchangeably, they have quite different meanings. Positive discrimination means giving preference, in this context, to a racial group over another *just because of* their race. This is unlawful under current legislation. Positive action refers to *acts* aimed at helping

improve the representation of particular groups with protected characteristics. This might include, for example, workshops to improve application writing and can be targeted at specific groups where they have been found to require support. However, those same groups cannot then be prioritized over others during the actual application process. For a comprehensive, accessible overview see Chapter 12, Equality & Human Rights Commission (2011).

2 See Reeves, Friedman, Rahal & Flemmen (2017) for a fascinating analysis of the relationship between elite private schooling, attendance at Oxbridge and membership of private members' clubs as a channel to elite recruitment. They ultimately argue that attending such schools has a 'propulsive power' in terms of facilitating networks and access to elite positions: 'Alumni of elite schools also retain a striking capacity to enter the elite even without passing through other prestigious institutions, such as Oxford, Cambridge, or private members clubs.'

3 Bourdieu, P. (1979) *Distinction: A Social Critique of the Judgement of Taste* (Abingdon: Routledge).

4 Bourdieu maintains that we can understand taste not just as the manifestation of what we deem acceptable but also as being informed by *the rejection* of that which provokes our disgust. These manifestations become a normalized, unquestioned expression of our ways of thinking and being. He conveys this point powerfully in his classic text *Distinction* (1979: 56):

> In matters of taste, more than anywhere else, all determination is negation; and tastes are perhaps first and foremost distastes, disgust provoked by the horror or visceral intolerance [. . .] of the tastes of others. [. . .] each taste feels itself to be natural – and so it almost is, being a habitus – which amounts to rejecting others as unnatural and therefore vicious.

5 Fanon makes this point powerfully in his damning book *Black Skins, White Masks*. He shows how what he describes as 'the fact of Blackness' haunts the Negro [*sic*] irrespective even of his middle-class status:

> It was always the Negro teacher, the Negro doctor; brittle as I was becoming, I shivered at the slightest pretext. I knew, for instance,

that if the physician made a mistake it would be the end of him and of all those who came after him. What could one expect, after all, from a Negro physician? As long as everything went well, he was praised to the skies, but look out, no nonsense, under any conditions! The black physician can never be sure how close he is to disgrace. I tell you I was walled in: No exception was made for my refined manners, or my knowledge of literature, or my understanding of quantum theory. (1967: 88–9)

6 This point is well documented in the literature on whiteness: 'Because the dominant norms of whiteness are not visible to them, whites are free to see themselves as "individuals" rather than as members of a culture. Individualism in turn becomes part of white resistance to perceiving whiteness and indeed to being placed in the category "white" at all.' (Martha Mahoney, 1997: 331)

7 Iris M. Young (2011) offers a useful, in-depth analysis of arguments about group identities and differences. See, in particular, Chapter Six, *Justice and the Politics of Difference*.

4: 'Keep A-Knocking But You Can't Come In'

1 A 2016 report examining the reasons for the underrepresentation of Black and minority ethnic employees concluded:

[. . .] high flying [Black and minority ethnic] individuals are not flying high enough, relative to their qualification, skills and experience, and they should be in positions of greater responsibility and leadership. In some instances, this is the result of closed, insular cultures in which people would be slightly taken aback at the idea that the boss might be anything other than a middle-class white man – knowing this, the white boss, in the end, picks a successor who is more or less familiar in appearance, manner, background, outlook and values. Elsewhere, the formal systems that sit behind hiring and promotion exercises can contain hidden biases that dilute the chances of minorities getting through. (Saggar et al., 2016: 16)

2 For example, see Wood et al. (2009) and Bertrand & Mullainathan (2004). In the latter study, the authors report that white candidates with a high-quality résumé (for example, more experience, fewer holes in their employment history, an email address, degree certification, evidence of language skills) were more likely to be called for an interview than white candidates with low-quality résumés. However, this was not the case for their African American counterparts:

> Race also affects the reward to having a better resume. Whites with higher-quality resumes receive nearly 30-percent more callbacks than Whites with lower-quality resumes. On the other hand, having a higher-quality resume has a smaller effect for African-Americans. In other words, the gap between Whites and African-Americans widens with resume quality. While one may have expected improved credentials to alleviate employers' fear that African-American applicants are deficient in some unobservable skills, this is not the case in our data. (Bertrand & Mullainathan, 2004: 992)

3 See Smith (2016).

Interlude: *Committed to Equality & Diversity*

1 Along with arguments that situate the lack of ethnic diversity in organizations as 'a pipeline issue', this is one of the phrases that causes me to bristle. It reveals a certain complacency and disengagement with one of the fundamental principles of anti-racism: taking action. Further, it highlights the casual disregard of the speaker in relation to their own privilege and power because it implies an acceptance of a status quo that does not disadvantage them. Put a different way, I cannot, as a Black woman, afford to nonchalantly come to the view that racism is just part of the tapestry of society and end my analysis there. I must find ways to understand it, to survive, to navigate the barriers thrown up by racism, to support my children and my children's children through the quagmire of racial injustice. Those who look like me are, by and large, forced to deal with this societal ill. We do not have the luxury of merely dismissing it.

5: The Christmas Party

1 Between the 1950s and 1970s, it was common for babies and children of West African heritage (most notably Nigerian and Ghanaian) to be placed by their parents in foster care with white families in the UK. This meant parents could work or study while their children were being looked after elsewhere. These paid private arrangements were facilitated through advertisements in print publications such as the childcare journal *Nursery World*. The children eventually returned to their families, sometimes many years later. For further discussion, see Bailkin (2009); Holman (2000).

2 Once again, Bourdieu's work is helpful here. He maintains that membership to a group is predicated on two layers of criteria: those which are explicitly named or set out (for example, in an application form) and those which are secondary or implicit but nonetheless regarded as important:

> The members of groups based on co-option [. . .] always have something else in common beyond the characteristics explicitly demanded. [. . .] those secondary characteristics [. . .] though absent from the official job description, function as tacit requirements, such as age, sex, social, or ethnic origin, overtly or implicitly guiding co-option choices, from entry into the profession and right through a career, so that members of the corps who lack these traits are excluded or marginalised [. . .] (1979: 103)

3 See Chapter 9, *Default to White*.

4 This, of course, is indicative of the practice of 'divide and rule'. In 2012, Labour MP Diane Abbott responded to a tweet by the Black journalist Bim Adewunmi, stating that white people love to 'divide and rule' and that Black people should not fall for their tactics. She added the hashtag #tacticsasoldascolonialism. Abbott was forced to apologize following the outcry provoked by the tweet. However, it is a tactic with which many Black people within majority white environments are familiar. The backlash provoked by Abbott's comment speaks directly to the characteristics of whiteness, namely, the rejection of a worldview other than one deemed palatable to a white majority

audience. People of colour are forced – at least publicly – to accept this interpretation of events over their own. For conflicting arguments regarding Abbott's tweet, see Pandya (2012) and Sparrow (2012).

6: V.O.Y.E.U.R.

1 The Combahee River Collective was a movement of Black lesbians based in Boston, USA who, in their struggle against 'racial, sexual, heterosexual and class oppression' advocated an understanding that 'major systems of oppression were interlocking'. This, of course, resonates with the now popular concept of 'intersectionality' initially introduced to the academic arena by the legal scholar and activist Kimberlé Crenshaw (1989, 1991):

> Although racism and sexism readily intersect in the lives of real people, they seldom do in feminist and antiracist practices. And so, when the practices expound identity as woman or person of color as an either/or proposition, they relegate the identity of women of color to a location that resists telling. (1991: 1242)

2 Common examples concern being surprised at how articulate or well spoken a person of colour is, the implication being that such levels of education or knowledge are an anomaly. Racial microaggressions can also appear to be positive or well meaning but the basis of the comment or observation betrays a naivety and heightened intrigue with an aspect of identity or culture that might be less well known to a white person. See Sue, Capodilupo & Holder (2008).

3 See Chapter 8, *A Special Kind of Madness* where I explore these tensions further.

4 As Crenshaw (1989: 144) explains: 'For white women, claiming sex discrimination is simply a statement that but for gender, they would not have been disadvantaged. For them there is no need to specify discrimination as *white* females because their race does not contribute to the disadvantage for which they seek redress.' However, white women committed to an inclusive understanding of feminism must be equally cognizant of the ways in which their racialized identity

proffers advantage and not just that this is moderated differently for women of colour but how white women often work in ways which are oppressive to them.

5 Feminists of colour in the UK made similar arguments. For example, see Valerie Amos and Pratibhar Parmar's (1984: 4) well-referenced article published in *Feminist Review* in which they state: 'our concern here is to show that white, mainstream feminist theory, be it from the socialist feminist or radical feminist perspective, does not speak to the experiences of Black women and where it attempts to do so it is often from a racist perspective and reasoning.'

6 Vron Ware (2015: 241) shows how the hierarchy between white and Black women is historically located. She documents the tense exchange which ensued when the anti-lynching activist and campaigner Ida B. Wells challenged the temperance reformer and suffragist Frances Willard about her lack of support for the anti-lynching movement:

> Although at one level [Willard and her followers] declared that they had no problem with the demand for racial equality, in practice they were unable to face up to the implications of their own political doctrines on the oppression of women. [. . .] they insisted that black men were still higher than white women in the hierarchy of gender dominance, and were reluctant to admit that white women domi-nated black men as well as black women in the hierarchy of race relations. Their anger came in part from the fact that it was a Black woman, whose social position was at the bottom of both systems of dominance, who was challenging them most insistently.

This anger and resistance to the experiences and knowledge base of Black women remains relevant today albeit in often more subtle forms of exclusion and assertions of power.

7 Such tropes are less commonly associated with Black women who tend, by contrast, to be described as strong, resilient, angry and emo-tionless (Reynolds, 1997).

8 Rollock, Vincent, Gillborn & Ball (2014) funded by the Economic and Social Research Council (RES 062 23 1880).

9 Accapadi, M. M. (2007) 'When white women cry: how white wom-en's tears oppress women of colour', *The College Students' Affairs Journal*, 26 (2), pp. 208–15.

10 Phipps (2021: 84) concedes that 'white feminists have been slower to acknowledge our own tendency to be lachrymose, which is often an attempt to avoid accountability in response to criticism by women of colour'.

11 Phipps, A. (2021) 'White tears, white rage: victimhood and (as) violence in mainstream feminism', *European Journal of Cultural Studies*, 24(1), p.84.

12 Black hair is often the subject of unsolicited interrogation and regulation as reflected, for example, in a number of school-related cases which have made the headlines in recent years. These include incidents in which Black pupils have been reprimanded for wearing their hair in natural styles that their schools have deemed to contravene their policies (Maxwell, 2020; Rigby, 2019).

However, there has been a concerted pushback against such incidents and negative portrayal. This includes an advertising campaign run by Project Embrace featuring Black men and women with natural hairstyles which aimed to 'show young black girls that their hair is beautiful. That they should never feel the need to give in to pressure about changing their hair or feel anxious about its texture.' In addition, Emma Dabiri's book *Don't Touch My Hair* (2020) highlights the history of Black hairstyling and challenges some of the misconceptions about it. And the Halo Collective, an activist youth movement in the UK, has launched the Halo Code to fight for a future without afro hair discrimination. The Code offers advice and information to schools and workplaces about afro-textured hair, culture and traditions to encourage increased understanding and acceptance. A number of companies have signed up to the Code as part of inclusion initiatives to show their support of Black hairstyles in the workplace. The Collective is also advocating for a change in the law so that hair discrimination is explicitly named in the Equality Act 2010.

7: Nigel's Story

1 In 2014, boys at a leavers' event at Bishop Vesey's Grammar School in Sutton Coldfield turned up in 'slave attire', some wearing chains

while others acted as their masters. According to a report in a local newspaper, *Birmingham Live*, photographs were taken of the boys posing with some of their teachers. The school later said it 'deeply regretted' the incident.

2 At Sacajawea Middle School in Spokane, in the US state of Washington, an investigation was carried out following a complaint that a teacher had instructed students to pick cotton as part of a class activity to better understand slavery. The report into the incident concluded that the teacher had not intended any harm toward the only two Black pupils in the class (Dodd, 2021a).

3 In November 2019, the British Psychological Society (BPS) hosted a conference dinner at the University of Liverpool which featured a re-enactment of a slave auction. According to the *Independent* newspaper, which reported the event, conference organizers had taken their inspiration from a similar enactment staged at Liverpool's International Slavery Museum but had failed to warn attendees in advance or take account of the different context of the conference and the potential offence the staging would cause to those (particularly of African and Caribbean heritage) in attendance. The BPS organizing committee subsequently published a statement apologizing for their actions:

> With some considerable regret, we acknowledge that we had not thought sufficiently about how the 'Capoeira for All' performance would be received, particularly given the focus allocated in the conference on discrimination in selection and pervasive issues with racism and Whiteness in clinical psychology in general.
>
> We acknowledge that we did not view the performance beforehand. Consequently, we were not fully aware of the overall emotional tone and power of the performance as a whole.
>
> We also acknowledge that we could have consulted with the Minorities Group about our decision-making. None of our decision-making should in any way be seen as a reflection on the politics and professionalism of 'Capoeira for All'. (University of Liverpool's Doctorate in Clinical Psychology GTiCP annual conference organising committee, 2019)

4   The experience of many Black people in the UK that it is easier to achieve success in the US is borne out by recent articles in the *Guardian* which focus on the rise of Black actors such as Idris Elba, David Harewood and Marianne Jean-Baptiste since moving Stateside, and *British Blacklist*, whose article looks at trends and success for Black music artists. An empirical study funded by AdvanceHE found that Black, Asian and minority ethnic scholars were more likely than their white counterparts to consider leaving the UK to work overseas in order to support their career advancement (Bhopal, Brown & Jackson, 2015).

5   Much is made about such individuals acting as 'role models' to future generations. I have two related discomforts about this. The first is captured in the following extract by Richard Delgado (1991: 1228):

> The job of role model requires that you lie – that you tell not little, but big, whopping lies, and that is bad for your soul. Suppose I am sent to an inner-city school to talk to the kids and serve as role model of the month. I am expected to tell the kids that if they study hard and stay out of trouble, they can become a law professor like me. That, however, is a very big lie: a whopper. When I started teaching law sixteen years ago, there were about thirty-five Hispanic law professors, approximately twenty-five of which were Chicano. Today, the numbers are only slightly improved. In the interim, however, a nearly complete turnover has occurred. The faces are new, but the numbers have remained the same from year to year. Gonzalez leaves teaching; Velasquez is hired somewhere else. Despite this, I am expected to tell forty kids in a crowded, inner-city classroom that if they work hard, they can each be among the chosen twenty-five.

This brings me to my second point, when I am asked about being a role model or my achievements, I counter by explaining that my journey has not been without its challenges and, depending on the setting, I may describe some of these, outline their emotional toll and how I worked to address them. I do this for two reasons: first, following Delgado, I want to problematize the idea of the two-dimensional role model as a special case who others can simply mirror to achieve success. The data simply does not bear this out.

Second, by sharing my experiences of how I have coped with knock-backs, I hope to normalize the idea that challenge is a part of everyday life and so encourage problem-solving and resilience amongst others. It means sharing practical tools to help manage adversity rather than the false promise of a straightforward road to success.

6 The feminist scholar Sara Ahmed (2009: 41) summarizes this well:

> If only we had the power we are imagined to possess, if only our proximity could be such a force. If only our arrival was their undo-ing [. . .] The argument is too much to sustain when your body is so exposed [. . .]

7 Social interactions within the workplace are rarely neutral. They matter because they expose patterns of dominance and power, privilege and oppression between groups.

> Relations of dominance, then, and of necessity struggles against them, are not theoretical abstractions, somewhere out there in an ethereal sphere unconnected to daily life. Rather they are based on and built out of an entire network of daily social and cultural relations and practices. Dominance depends on both leadership and legitimation. (Apple, 2012: xxiv)

8 Cited in Russell (2019).
9 *Architectural Record* (2021).

8: A Special Kind of Madness

1 Responding in 2019 to the government's announcement on tackling racial disparities at universities, Russell Group Chief Executive Dr Tim Bradshaw said:

> Russell Group universities run programmes to attract and support BME students and staff, from outreach work with schools to mentoring, reviewing curricula and campus culture and providing targeted support for early career researchers. While the picture varies across individual universities and for different ethnic groups,

recent years have seen important progress. [. . .] However, it is clear that serious challenges remain and black students, in particular, continue to be underrepresented. (Russell Group, 2019)

2   In 2020, the Royal Mail painted four letter boxes black – one in each of the four countries of the UK – in honour of Black History Month. The gesture was met with ridicule by some activists who criticized the move as superficial especially in light of its all-white board (Young, 2020; Rawlinson, 2020).

3   The white anti-racist scholar Bree Picower (2009) uses the term the 'tools of whiteness' to describe the collective acts that keep white priorities and perspectives in the spotlight.

4   In their paper 'Pedagogy of fear', Leonardo & Porter (2010: 140) explain the impossibility of safety for racially minoritized groups in racial dialogue with white people:

> In public settings, people of color find themselves between the Scylla of becoming visible and the Charybdis of remaining silent. If minorities follow an analytics of color, they run the risk of incurring white symbolic racism at best or literal violence at worst. Although some may argue that people of color maintain their dignity and counteract the culture of silence when they come to voice, participating in public race dialogue makes them vulnerable to assaults on many fronts. On one level their actions illuminate what Fanon characterized as the tenuous relationship between humanity and reason. [. . .] On another level, by sharing their real perspectives on race, minorities become overt targets of personal and academic threats. It becomes a catch-22 for them. Either they must observe the safety of whites and be denied a space that promotes people of color's growth and development or insist on a space of integrity and put themselves further at risk not only of violence, but also risk being conceived of as illogical or irrational.

5   Sara Ahmed (2012: 144) puts this well: 'The response to a complaint about racism and how [the institution] handles the complaint [. . .] takes the form of an assertion of organisational pride. [. . .] The response to the complaint enacts the very problem that the complaint is about.'

237

6 This sits in line with discussions in earlier chapters about how those in power work to hold on to it and, in so doing, often rationalize the oppression of marginalized groups: 'In order to justify hierarchy, those in power have to suggest a less than human status for those who do not fit into their racial group. And the boundaries of that racial group must be tightly guarded.' (Ladson-Billings, 2020: 20)

9: Default to White

1 I am drawing here on the work of scholars such as Michael Apple and Stephen Ball whose analysis largely focuses on interrogating power relations within the education context and the impact of policies within those spaces. Following Apple (2004:10), I am interested in 'what social and economic groups and classes seem to be helped by the way institutions in our society are organized and controlled and which groups are not'.

2 The word 'fit' is often invoked in feedback to unsuccessful candidates following job interviews. For example: 'it was a close call, but we felt the candidate we offered the position to was a better fit'. The vagueness of the word is useful to the organization as it hides a myriad of possible truths it does not care to openly declare and leaves the candidate none the wiser in terms of their performance. 'Fit' can also act as a fuzzy signifier representing unspoken cultural norms and practices that tend to extend beyond the formally sanctioned requirements and criteria of the role.

3 See Carbado & Gulati (2013).

4 The concept of *protectionism* is often associated with economics and trade, but I argue that it can also be applied to racial dynamics and how organizational policies and processes operate to the advantage of those already in positions of power within them.

10: *Darker than Blue*

1 The inspiration for the title for this chapter comes from the Curtis Mayfield song 'We the People Who Are Darker Than Blue' in which Mayfield implores Black people to unite in order to continue the fight for racial justice (Shonekan, 2017). 'Darker than blue' speaks to an appreciation of Black skin in its deepest melanin hue. This can be considered a re-owning or reclaiming of Blackness within a postcolonial context where being Black is otherwise deemed ugly, problematic and undesirable. Useful to the themes in this chapter, the colour blue is also associated with the dark navy uniform of UK and US police. It is also conveyed via the colloquial phrase 'blues and twos' to denote the blue flashing lights and two-tone siren used on police cars and other emergency vehicles.

2 The Independent Office for Police Conduct oversees complaints against the police in England and Wales. Their website explains that: 'We investigate the most serious matters, including deaths following police contact, and set the standards by which the police should handle complaints. We use learning from our work to influence changes in policing. We are independent, and make our decisions entirely independently of the police and government.'

3 Although the majority of homicide victims are white, when taking account of different population sizes, Black people had higher rates of victimization compared with other ethnic groups in the three years to end March 2021. For details see Office for National Statistics (2022).

4 Police in the UK use Tasers (controlled electronic devices) to 'temporarily incapacitate a subject through use of an electrical current which temporarily interferes with the body's neuromuscular system and produces a sensation of intense pain' (College of Policing). There have been several stories in the press about the impact and allegedly improper use of this police tool particularly on Black men. For a detailed overview of Tasers and the impact of electricity on the body see Bleetman, Steyn & Lee (2004).

5 The National Association for the Advancement of Colored People is a US-based organization set up in 1909, with a strong and very active legal arm, that works to improve the rights of Black people.

6 About six months after completing this chapter, I was alerted to an article in the *Guardian* with the headline 'Black people more likely to be Tasered for longer, police watchdog finds' (Dodd, 2021b). I read it and then went to check the source of the data: the Independent Office for Police Conduct (IOPC). The report documents their findings following a review of 101 independent IOPC cases involving the use of Tasers from 1 April 2015 to 31 March 2020. As well as finding that Black people were more likely to be subjected to Taser use compared to white and Asian people, it revealed:

> [. . .] 29% of White people involved in Taser discharges were subjected to continuous discharges of more than five seconds, whereas 60% of Black people involved in Taser discharges were subjected to continuous discharges of more than five seconds. As such, while Black people were less likely to be involved in Taser discharges, when they were, they were more likely to be tasered for prolonged periods. (IOPC, 2021)

7 The idea of poor practice in policing and data manipulation is not as fanciful as I have implied. In 2020, the then Chief Constable of Greater Manchester Police, Ian Hopkins, resigned following an inspection that revealed that the force had failed to record a phenomenal 80,100 crimes in a year (HMICFRS, 2020).

Her Majesty's Inspectorate of Constabulary (now known as HMICFRS to incorporate the fire and rescue services) is the body responsible for carrying out inspections of individual police forces. However, while it can identify areas for improvement, it has no powers of enforcement.

Police and Crime Commissioners are elected, independent individuals whose principal responsibility is to hold their local police chief constable to account. There are individual PCCs for each of the police forces in England and Wales. For more information, see Home Office (n.d.).

8 In an interview in 2020 for BBC Radio 4's *Woman's Hour* about racism and white people in the months following the murder of George Floyd, the podcaster and journalist Otegha Uwagba described how her book entitled *The Little Black Book* was suddenly catapulted on to

reading lists about anti-racism. The book in fact provides tips and strategies for women – of any colour – about how to manage and navigate their careers.

9 Black teenager Anthony Walker was murdered in an unprovoked racist attack in Huyton, Liverpool in 2005. For details including a timeline of events, see Press Association (2005). A foundation has been set up in his memory.

The Persistence of the Racial Code

1 Fanon, F. (1967) *Black Skin, White Masks* (London: Pluto Press), p.87.
2 I am interested in how people of colour achieve success despite the challenges presented by racism. This connects with the work of writers such as Fanon and DuBois who have debated the notion of duality for the Black man [*sic*] as he works to forge an existence within mainstream white society and how this contrasts with and informs existence within the company of those who look like him. These two states are in constant tension for they rarely align (or do so under very particular conditions), for in order to survive, people of colour must – even at a subconscious level – find ways to tolerate and navigate white spaces:

> People of color sometimes overlook white violence so they can get through their daily life. Like a child who has been abused, people of color avoid white violence by strategically playing along, a practice that whites, whose racial development stunts their growth, underestimate when they mistake consensus as the absence of coercion. Like abused children who do not possess the ability to consent and defend themselves against the verbal and physical power of a parent, people of color have become masters at deflection. This is how they secure safety in violent circumstances. (Leonardo & Porter, 2010: 151)

3 Racism is not static or fixed. It is shaped, for example, by social mores, activism and changes to legislation. When explaining this to my students, I often show an image of the 'no dogs, no Irish, no Blacks' signs of the 1960s. Just because we no longer see such signs

241

blatantly displayed in windows today does not automatically mean the inhabitants are embracing of racial justice. That is, we have become adept at suppressing and reformulating explicit views about racism and racial difference into that which is more ambiguous, less easily identified. The African American scholar Gloria Ladson-Billings (1998: 9) explains:

> [. . .] our conceptions of race, even in a postmodern and/or post-colonial world, are more embedded and fixed than in a previous age. However, this embeddedness or 'fixed-ness' has required new language and constructions of race so that denotations are submerged and hidden in ways that are offensive though without identification. [. . .] Conceptual categories like 'school achievement', 'middle classness', 'maleness', 'beauty', 'intelligence,' and 'science' become normative categories of whiteness, while categories like 'gangs', 'welfare recipients', 'basketball players,' and 'the underclass' become the marginalized and de-legitimated categories of blackness.

4 Again, we return to the work of Leonardo (2009: 115): '[Whites project] [. . .] racialism onto people of color, removing themselves as alibis, or non-racial spectators, rather than participants in the racialization process. In other words, whites often play the race card as a sign of their investment in whiteness and as a way to direct the public discourse in terms acceptable to them.'

5 Narcissistic abuse is characterized by the repeated, toxic foregrounding of the needs and interests of the perpetrator:

> One of the more frequently studied consequential interpersonal behaviors of narcissism is the perpetration of aggression following ego threats. Theories have postulated the concept of 'narcissistic injury' in explaining how narcissistic self-preoccupation can fuel a vicious cycle of intense anger, violence, and vindictiveness when self-esteem is challenged. [. . .] when the potential of a threat (real or imagined) is perceived by the narcissist, intolerable emotions in the form of shame, humiliation, and anger are evoked, followed either instantly or later by a self-righteous defensive response

intended to attack or eliminate the source of threat to restore self-esteem. (Green & Charles, 2019: 2)

The emotional reactions listed here correspond with those cited in the academic literature about white people's responses to race, racism and cultural diversity.

6   Coates, T. (2015) *Between the World and Me* (Australia: The Text Publishing Company), p.97.

7   I have become increasingly interested in the subject of denial while writing this book. Cohen's (2001) work is particularly relevant to the arguments I have detailed. He defines denial as 'an unconscious defence mechanism for coping with guilt, anxiety and other disturbing emotions aroused by reality' (p. 5). It manifests in three fundamental ways: actual or literal, interpretive and implicatory. *Literal denial* is 'the assertion that something did not happen or is not true'. In the context of *The Racial Code* we might therefore say: 'the racism you say you experienced did not happen'; the person is being falsely accused. *Interpretative denial* is the acceptance of the basic fact that the incident or event happened, but the meaning or interpretation of the incident is called into question and ultimately rejected. This form of denial recognizes that we both saw the same incident but the way that one person interpreted it is wrong. In the context of racism, this can leave people of colour in a perpetual state of needing to provide more and more evidence in order to convince white people that racism has actually occurred. Given my argument about racism only existing in the form defined by white people, we can see how inherently complex and potentially never-ending this might be. Finally, *implicatory denial*, as the name indicates, refers to the implications inferred from the interpretation of what happened. That is, there is acknowledgement that the incident occurred, or the facts are as stated, and the interpretation is accepted but the *impact or consequences* of the incidence are minimized or rejected. One way to think about this is as a form of dismissal, minimizing or reframing: I agree that you fell over (literal agreement with the fact) and that it hurts (interpretative) but I do not agree that it warrants your tears (implicatory).

8 This is similar to James Baldwin's description of white people as having 'opted for being white' (1985: 34). This usefully draws attention to the collective set of historically situated, learnt behaviours, processes and presumptions that underpin whiteness even while they themselves claim to have difficulty seeing or recognizing these as constitutive of a discernible white identity and norms.

9 As the white anti-racism scholar David Gillborn explains (2005: 488):

> Critical scholarship on whiteness is not an assault on white people per se: it is an assault on the socially constructed and constantly reinforced power of white identifications and interests [. . .]. 'So-called "White" people' (Bonnett, 1997, p. 189) do not necessarily reinforce whiteness any more than heterosexual people are necessarily homophobic, or men are necessarily sexist. However, these analogies are useful because they highlight the forces that recreate and extend the kinds of 'unthinking' assumptions and actions which mean that very many (probably the majority) of heterosexuals are homophobic and most men are sexist. It is possible for white people to take a real and active role in deconstructing whiteness but such 'race traitors' are relatively uncommon.

10 I sometimes play with this argument via a thought experiment when I am listening to BBC Radio 4's *Woman's Hour*. I swap each occurrence of 'woman' with 'Black' (or 'people of colour') and replace 'men' with 'white' and rerun, as it were, the point or topic under discussion. I am often struck by how impossible it would be to have the conversation on the same topic if the focus were on race. While, of course, it is not empirical research and I am certainly not implying there is now a level playing field for women, it does help, in a very accessible way, demonstrate our relative confidence and progress regarding matters concerning women.

11 In making this argument, I draw on Young's (2011) work about the relationship between privileged and oppressed groups: 'The privileged usually are not inclined to protect or advance the interests of the oppressed, partly because their social position prevents them from understanding those interests, and partly because to some

degree their privilege depends on the continued oppression of others.' (p. 185)

12 Kegler (2016) argues:

> [. . .] most White people can't handle talking about racism. [. . .] To mitigate our shortcomings, we surround ourselves with comforting words. Words that feel neutral. Words that don't point fingers (at us). Words that center Whiteness, while erasing the harshness of discrimination and segregation. We reject words that we feel are too direct, that might reveal complicity on our part.

13 This is commonplace in higher education. A press release will state that the university has promoted the 'youngest Black professor within [a particular group of universities]' or the 'first Black professor in [subject specialism]' when the subject specialism was only recently introduced or there are in fact no other Black professors at the university or at comparable institutions.

14 Ladson-Billings, G. (2020) 'Who's black? Hybridity, complexity, and fluidity in 21st-century racial identity', in Robert T. Teranishi, Bach Mai Dolly Nguyen, Edward R. Curammeng, Cynthia M. Alcantar (eds), *Measuring Race: Why Disaggregating Data Matters for Addressing Educational Inequality* (New York: Teachers' College, Columbia University), p.19.

15 This point is powerfully conveyed by Derrick Bell (1992:13):

> The goal of racial equality is, while comforting to many whites, more illusory than real for blacks. For too long we have worked for substantive reform, then settled for weakly worded and poorly enforced legislation, indeterminate judicial decisions, token government positions, even holidays. I repeat. If we are to seek new goals for our struggles, we must first reassess the worth of the racial assumptions on which, without careful thought, we have presumed too much and relied on too long.

References

Abbey, N. (2019) *Think Like a White Man: A Satirical Guide to Conquering the World . . . While Black* (Edinburgh: Canongate)

Accapadi, M. M. (2007) 'When white women cry: How white women's tears oppress women of colour', *The College Students' Affairs Journal*, 26 (2), pp. 208–15

Adichie, Chimamanda Ngozi (2013) *Americanah* (London: 4th Estate)

Ahmed, S. (2009) 'Embodying diversity: Problems and paradoxes for Black feminists', *Race Ethnicity & Education*, 12(1), pp. 41–52

Ahmed, S. (2012) *On Being Included: Racism and Diversity in Institutional Life* (Durham, NC: Duke University Press)

Akala (2018) *Natives* (London: Hodder & Stoughton)

Amos, V. & Parmar, P. (1984) 'Challenging imperial feminism', *Feminist Review*, 17, pp. 3–19

Ansley, F. L. (1997) 'White supremacy (and what we should do about it)', in: R. Delgado & J. Stefancic (eds.), *Critical White Studies: Looking Behind the Mirror* (Philadelphia: Temple University Press), pp. 592–5

Apple, M. W. (2004) *Ideology and Curriculum*, 3rd Edition (London & New York: Routledge)

Apple, M. W. (2012) *Education and Power* (London & New York: Routledge)

Architectural Record (2021) 'Lesley Lokko explains her resignation from City College of New York's Spitzer School of Architecture', 5 October

Ashe, S. & Nazroo, J. (2016) *Equality, Diversity and Racism in the Workplace: A Qualitative Analysis of the 2015 Race at Work Survey*, ESRC Centre on Dynamics of Ethnicity, University of Manchester

Badenoch, K. (2020) Black History Month, *Hansard*, Volume 682; column 1011

Bailkin, J. (2009) 'The postcolonial family? West African children, private fostering, and the British state', *The Journal of Modern History*, 81, pp. 87–121

Baldwin, J. (1985) *Dark Days* (London: Penguin)

Baldwin, J. (1985) *The Price of the Ticket*, reprinted (2018) *Dark Days* (London: Penguin)

Ball, S., Maguire, M. & Braun, A. (2012) *How Schools Do Policy: Policy Enactments in Secondary Schools* (London & New York: Routledge)

Bandyopadhyay, R. (2019) '"The white man's burden": Globalization of suffering, white saviour complex, religion and modernity', *Journal of Sustainable Tourism*, 27(3), pp. 327–43

Banton, M. (1969) 'Social aspects of the race question', in UNESCO (eds.) *Four Statements on the Race Question* (Paris: United Nations Educational, Scientific and Cultural Organisation)

Barmes, L. (2022) 'Silencing at work: Sexual harassment, workplace misconduct and NDAs', *Industrial Law Journal*, 51

BBC News (2009) 'Met is "no longer racist" – Straw', Sunday 22 February

BBC News (2008) 'Bias "would hamper British Obama"', Saturday 8 November

BBC *Woman's Hour* (12 November 2020) https://www.bbc.co.uk/sounds/play/m000p8cg

Bell, D. (1992) *Faces at the Bottom of the Well: The Permanence of Racism.* (New York: Basic Books).

Bell, K. (2013) 'Raising Africa?: Celebrity and the rhetoric of the white saviour', *Journal of Multidisciplinary International Studies*, 10(1), pp. 1–24

Bertrand, M. & Mullainathan, S. (2004) 'Are Emily and Greg more employable than Lakisha and Jamal? A field experiment on labour market discrimination', *American Economic Review*, September, pp. 991–1013

Bhambra, G. K., Gebrial, D. & Nisancioglu, K. (2018) *Decolonising the University?* (London: Pluto Press)

Bhopal, K., Brown, H. & Jackson, J. (2015) *Academic Flight: How to Encourage Black and Minority Ethnic Academics to Stay in UK Higher Education*, Research Report (London: ECU)

Bleetman, A., Steyn, R. & Lee, C. (2004) 'Introduction of the Taser into British policing. Implications for UK emergency departments: An overview of electronic weaponry', *Emergency Medicine Journal*, 21, pp. 136–40, https://emj.bmj.com/content/21/2/136.full

Bonnett, A. (1997) 'Constructions of whiteness in European and American anti-racism', in: P. Werbner & T. Modood (Eds) *Debating cultural hybridity: multi-cultural identities and the politics of anti-racism* (London: Zed Books).

Bourdieu, P. (1979) *Distinction: A Social Critique of the Judgement of Taste* (Abingdon: Routledge)

Bourdieu, P. (1986) 'The forms of capital', in J. G. Richardson (ed.), *Handbook of Theory and Research for the Sociology of Education* (New York: Greenwood Press), pp. 241–58

Bourdieu, P. (1990b) *In Other Words: Essays Towards a Reflexive Sociology* (Cambridge: Polity Press)

Boudreau, V. (2021) 'Statement on Dean Lokko's resignation', City College of New York, Office of the President

Bunglawala, Z. (2019) 'Please, don't call me BAME or BME!', *Civil Service Blog*, 8 July

Business in the Community (BiTC) (2015) *Race at Work Survey* (London: BiTC)

Carbado, D. & Gulati, M. (2013) *Acting White: Rethinking Race in 'Post-Racial' America* (New York: Oxford University Press)

Carby, H. (1982) 'White woman listen! Black feminism and the boundaries of sisterhood', in Centre for Contemporary Cultural Studies, *The Empire Strikes Back: Race and Racism in 70s Britain* (London: Hutchinson), pp. 212–35

Carmichael, S. & Hamilton, C. V. (1967) *Black Power: The Politics of Liberation in America* (London: Penguin)

Cashmore, E. & Jennings, J. (2001) (eds.) *Racism: Essential Readings* (London: SAGE)

Chaudhuri, A. (2016) 'The real meaning of Rhodes Must Fall', *The Guardian*, Wednesday 16 March

Coates, T. (2015) *Between the World and Me* (Melbourne: The Text Publishing Company)

Cohen, S. (2001) *States of Denial: Knowing about Atrocities and Suffering* (Cambridge & Malden, MA: Polity Press)

Cole, T. (2012) 'The white-savior industrial complex', *The Atlantic*, 21 March

Crenshaw, K. (1989) 'Demarginalizing the intersection of race and sex: A Black feminist critique of antidiscrimination doctrine, feminist theory and antiracist politics', *University of Chicago Legal Forum*, 1(8), pp. 139–69

Crenshaw, K. (1991) 'Mapping the margins: Intersectionality, identity politics, and violence against women of color', *Stanford Law Review*, 43 (6), pp. 1241–99

Crenshaw, K., Gotanda, N., Peller, G. & Thomas, K. (1996) *Critical Race Theory: The Key Writings that Formed the Movement* (New York: The New Press)

Dabiri, E. (2020) *Don't Touch My Hair* (London: Penguin Books)

Delgado, R. (1991) 'Affirmative action as a majoritarian device: or, do you really want to be a role model?', *Michigan Law Review*, 89(5), pp. 1222–31

Delgado, R. (2000) 'Storytelling for oppositionists and others: A plea for narrative', in R. Delgado, & J. Stefancic, (eds.) *Critical Race Theory: The Cutting Edge*, 2nd edition (Philadelphia, PA: Temple University Press), pp. 60–70

Delgado, R., & Stefancic, J. (2001) *Critical Race Theory: An Introduction* (New York & London: New York University Press)

Department for Business, Energy & Industrial Strategy (2019) 'Crack down on misuse of Non-Disclosure Agreements in the workplace', Press Release, 21 July

Di Stasio, V. & Heath, A. (2019) 'Are employers in Britain discriminating against ethnic minorities?' (Oxford: Centre for Social Investigation)

DiAngelo, R. (2011) 'White fragility', *International Journal of Critical Pedagogy*, 3(3), pp. 54–70

Dodd, A. (2021a) 'Cotton gin lesson at Sacajawea Middle School had no intent to harm, investigation finds', *The Spokesman-Review*, Friday 30 July

Dodd, V. (2009) 'Met no longer institutionally racist, says commissioner', *The Guardian*, Tuesday 24 February

Dodd, V. (2021b) 'Black people more likely to be Tasered for longer, police watchdog finds', *The Guardian*, Wednesday 25 August

Eddo-Lodge, R. (2016) *Why I Am No Longer Talking to White People about Race* (London: Bloomsbury)

Education Week (2021) 'Where Critical Race Theory is under attack', 11 June

Ellison, R. (1965) *Invisible Man* (Harmondsworth: Penguin Books)

Equality & Human Rights Commission (EHRC) (2011) *Employment Statutory Code of Practice* (London: EHRC)

Fakim, N. & Macaulay, C. (2020) '"Don't call me BAME": Why some people are rejecting the term', BBC News, 30 June

Fanon, F. (1967) *Black Skin, White Masks* (London: Pluto Press)

Gillborn, D. (2008) *Racism and Education: Coincidence or Conspiracy?* (Abingdon & New York: Routledge)

Gillborn, D. (2005) 'Education policy as an act of white supremacy: Whiteness, Critical Race Theory and education reform', *Journal of Education Policy*, 20(4), pp. 485–505

Green, A. & Charles, K. (2019) 'Voicing the victims of narcissistic partners: A qualitative analysis of responses to narcissistic injury and self-esteem regulation', *SAGE Open*, 9(2), pp. 1–10

Hall, S. (1995) 'New ethnicities', in B. Ashcroft, G. Griffiths & H. Tiffin (eds.), *The Post-Colonial Studies Reader* (New York & London: Routledge)

Hangartner, D., Kopp, D. & Siegenthaler, M. (2021) 'Monitoring hiring discrimination through online recruitment platforms', *Nature*, 589, pp. 572–6

Harker, J. (2017) 'Highest paid BBC stars are all white. Where's the outrage?', *The Guardian*, Thursday 20 July

Harts, M. (2019) '"Sally" in HR with actress Kelechi Okafor', CircleAround™, 20 February

Hinsliff, Gaby (2019) '"White saviours" belong in the 1980s. Let's keep them there', *The Guardian*, Thursday 28 February

HMICFRS (2020) 'Greater Manchester Police: An inspection of the service provided to victims of crime by Greater Manchester Police' (London: Her Majesty's Inspectorate of Constabulary and Fire & Rescue Services)

Holman, B. (2003) 'Private fostering: Old problems, new urgency', *Adoption & Fostering*, 27:3, pp. 8–18

Home Office (n.d.) 'Have you got what it takes? Your role as police and crime commissioner' (London: Home Office)

Home Office (2008) *Race Equality: The Home Secretary's Employment Targets*, Report 2007/08 Ninth Annual Report (London: Home Office)

Home Office (2021) 'Police workforce, England and Wales, 31 March 2020, 2nd edition' (London: Crown Copyright)

Home Affairs Committee (2021) *The Macpherson Report: Twenty-two Years On* (London: House of Commons)

Houser, K.A. (2019) 'Can AI solve the diversity problem in the tech industry? Mitigating noise and bias in employment decision-making', *Stanford Technology Law Review*, Spring, pp. 290–354

hooks, b. (1987) *Ain't I a Woman: Black Women and Feminism* (London: Pluto Press)

hooks, b. (1990) 'Yearning: race, gender and cultural politics', (Toronto, Ontario: Between the Lines)

hooks, b. (2000) *Feminist Theory: From Margin to Center* (London: Pluto Press)

IOPC (2021) *Review of IOPC Cases Involving the Use of Taser 2015–2020* (London: IOPC)

Kebede, A. & Knottnerus, J. D. (1998) 'Beyond the pales of Babylon: The ideational components and social psychological foundations of Rastafari', *Sociological Perspectives*, 41(3), pp. 499–517

Kegler, A. (2016) 'The sugarcoated language of white fragility', *Huffington Post*, 22 July

Kernohan, D. (2019) 'A beginner's guide to academic workload modelling', *Wonkhe*, 11 March

Lacy, K. (2007) *Blue-chip Black: Race, Class and Status in the New Black Middle Class* (California: University of California Press)

Ladson-Billings, G. (1998) 'Just what is Critical Race Theory and what's it doing in a nice field like education?', *International Journal of Qualitative Studies in Education*, 11, no. 1, pp. 7–24

Ladson-Billings, G. (2020) 'Who's black? Hybridity, complexity and fluidity in 21st-century racial identity', in R. T. Teranishi, B.M.D. Nguyen, E.R. Curammeng, C.M. Alcantar (eds.), *Measuring Race: Why Disaggregating Data Matters for Addressing Educational Inequality* (New York: Teachers' College, Columbia University)

Lammy, D. (2017) 'Africa deserves better from Comic Relief', *The Guardian*, Friday 24 March

Lawrence, D., with M. Busby (2006) *And Still I Rise: Seeking Justice for Stephen* (London: Faber & Faber)

Leathwood, C., Maylor, U. & Moreau, M-P. (2009) 'Experiences of Black and minority ethnic staff working in higher education: Literature review' (London: Equality Challenge Unit)

Leonardo, Z. (2009) *Race, Whiteness and Education*, Critical Thought Series (New York & Abingdon: Routledge)

Leonardo & Porter (2009) 'Pedagogy of fear: Toward a Fanonian theory of "safety" in race dialogue', *Race, Ethnicity & Education*, 13 (2), pp. 139–57

Lewis, H. (2020) 'The mythology of Karen', *The Atlantic*, 19 August

Lightfoot, L. (2000) 'Black culture "holding back" boys', *The Telegraph*, 21 August

Mahoney, M. (1997) 'The social construction of whiteness', in R. Delgado & J. Stefancic (eds.), *Critical White Studies: Looking Behind the Mirror* (Philadelphia: Temple University Press)

Macpherson, W. (1999) *The Stephen Lawrence Inquiry* (London: The Stationery Office)

Martin, G. (2019) 'Dooley accused of being a "white saviour" over Comic Relief film', *TFN*, 28 February

Matias, C. (2020) Introduction, in C. Matias (ed.), *Surviving Becky(s): Pedagogies for Deconstructing Whiteness and Gender* (Maryland & London: Lexington Books)

Maxwell, E. (2020) 'What next for schools after hair discrimination case?', *Schools Week*, Friday 21 February

McGregor-Smith, R. (2017) *Race in the Workplace: The McGregor-Smith Review* (London: Department for Business, Energy & Industrial Strategy)

Mieder, W. (2009) *'Yes We Can': Barack Obama's Proverbial Rhetoric* (New York: Peter Lang)

Mills, C. (1997) *The Racial Contract* (Cornell: Cornell University Press)

Mirror (2019) 'Stacey Dooley trolled for "white saviour complex" after Comic Relief trip to Uganda', *Daily Mirror*, 27 February

Morris, N. (2020) 'The emotional impact of watching white people wake up to racism in real time', *Metro*, Friday 12 June

Morrison, T. (1975) 'A humanist view'. Speech given at Portland State University, 30 May

Muir, H. (2014) 'Why do black actors like Idris Elba have to go to the US for success?', *The Guardian*, Sunday 24 January

Nagesth, A. (2020) 'What exactly is a "Karen" and where did the meme come from?' *BBC News*, 31 July

Office for National Statistics (ONS) (2022) *Homicide in England and Wales: Year Ending March 2021* (London: ONS)

Pandya, A, (2012) 'She's an expert in "divide and rule" if ever there was one', *The Daily Mail*, 8 January

Phillips, T. (2009) Stephen Lawrence speech: 'Institutions must catch up with public on race issues'. Speech given on 19 January, London

Phipps, A, (2021) 'White tears, white rage: Victimhood and (as) violence in mainstream feminism', *European Journal of Cultural Studies*, 24(1), pp. 81–93

Picower, B. (2009) 'The unexamined whiteness of teaching: How white teachers maintain and enact dominant racial ideologies', *Race Ethnicity & Education* 12 (2), pp. 197–215

Press Association (2005) 'Timeline: Anthony Walker murder', *The Guardian*, Wednesday 30 November

Rankine, C. (2020) *Just Us: An American Conversation* (London: Allen Lane)

Rawlinson, K. (2020) 'Activists criticise "tokenistic" efforts after rebrand of Royal Mail postboxes', *The Guardian*, Thursday 1 October

Reeves, A., Friedman, S., Rahal, C. & Flemmen, M. (2017) 'The decline and persistence of the old boy: Private schools and elite recruitment 1897 to 2016', *American Sociological Review*, 82(6), pp. 1139–66

Reynolds, T. (1997) '(Mis)representing the black (super)woman', in H. S. Mirza (ed.) *Black British Feminism: A Reader* (London & New York: Routledge)

Richardson, H. (2011) 'African-Caribbean boys "would rather hustle than learn"', *BBC News Online*, 21 October

Rigby, H. (2019) 'White teachers like me should not be policing black pupils' hair', *The Guardian*, Wednesday 22 May

Rollock, N. (2009) *The Stephen Lawrence Inquiry 10 Years On* (London: Runnymede Trust)

Rollock, N. (2014) 'Race, Class and the "harmony of dispositions"', *Sociology*, 48 (3), pp. 445–51

Rollock, N. (2019a) *Staying Power: The Career Strategies and Experiences of UK Black Female Professors* (London: UCU)

Rollock, N. (2019b) 'We urgently need more Black female professors in UK universities', *British Vogue*, 6 February

Rollock, N. (2021) '"I would have become wallpaper if racism had its way": Black female professors, racial battle fatigue and strategies to survive higher education', *Peabody Journal of Education*, 96(2), pp. 206–17

Rollock, N. & Gillborn, D. (2011) *Critical Race Theory (CRT)*, British Educational Research Association online resource

Rollock, N., Vincent, C., Gillborn, D. & Ball, S. (2014) *The Colour of Class: The Educational Strategies of the Black Middle Classes* (Abingdon & New York: Routledge)

Russell Group (2019) 'Tackling race disparities', https://russellgroup. ac.uk/news/tackling-racial-disparities/, 1 February

Russell, J.S. (2019) 'Lesley Lokko, global architect and novelist, appointed Architecture Dean at City College of New York', *Architectural Record*, 11 June

Saggar, S., Norrie, R., Bannister, M. & Goodhart, D. (2016) *Bittersweet Success? Glass Ceilings for Britain's Ethnic Minorities at the Top of Business and the Professions* (London: Policy Exchange)

Sawchuk, S. (2021) 'What is Critical Race Theory and why is it under attack?', *Education Week*, 18 May

Shonekan, S. (2017) 'Epilogue: "We People Who Are Darker Than Blue": Black studies and the Mizzou movement', *The Journal of Negro Education*, 86(3), pp. 399–404

Sini, R. (2016) 'Wear a weave at work – your afro hair is unprofessional', *BBC News*, 15 May

Sivanandan, A. (2000) 'The liberation of the Black intellectual', in K. Owusu (ed.), *Black British Culture & Society: A Text Reader* (London & New York: Routledge)

Smith, F. (2016) 'Anonymous recruitment aims to stamp out bias, but can it prevent discrimination?', *The Guardian*, Tuesday 5 July

Smith, W. A. (2004) 'Black faculty coping with racial battle fatigue: The campus racial climate in a post-civil rights era', in D. Cleveland (ed.), *A Long Way to Go: Conversations about Race by African American Faculty and Graduate Students* (New York: Peter Lang), pp. 171–90

Social Mobility & Child Poverty Commission (2014) *Elitist Britain?* (London: Social Mobility & Child Poverty Commission)

Sparrow, A. (2012) 'Diane Abbott apologises over Twitter racism row', *The Guardian*, 5 January

Spitzer (2019) 'Lesley Lokko named Dean', *News*, 6 July

Straw, J. (1999) 'Stephen Lawrence Inquiry', speech to Parliament by The Secretary of State for the Home Department, *House of Commons Hansard Archives* (online)

Sue, D., Capodilupo, C. M. & Holder, A. M. B. (2008) 'Racial microaggressions in the life experiences of Black Americans', *Professional Psychology: Research and Practice*, 39(3), p. 326

Sweet, P. L. (2019) 'The sociology of gaslighting', *American Sociological Review*, 84 (5), pp. 851–75

Tammy, V. (2013) 'Black British artists look to America for success?', *British Blacklist*, 30 May

Tate IV, W. F. (1997) 'Critical Race Theory and education: History, theory and implications', *Review of Research in Education*, 22, pp. 195–247

The Combahee River Collective (1995) 'A Black feminist statement', in B. Guy-Sheftall (ed.), *Words of Fire: An Anthology of African-American Feminist Thought* (New York: The New Press)

UNESCO (1969) 'Statement on race', Paris 1950 in UNESCO (eds.), *Four Statements on the Race Question* (Paris: United Nations Educational, Scientific and Cultural Organization)

University & College Union (UCU) (2012) 'The position of women and BME staff in professorial roles in UK HEIs' (London: UCU)

University of Liverpool's Doctorate in Clinical Psychology GTiCP annual conference organising committee (2019) 'A message for all GTiCP conference delegates', published online

Vasista, V. (2010) *'Snowy Peaks': ethnic diversity at the top* (London: Runnymede Trust)

Ware, V. (2015) *Beyond the Pale: White Women, Racism and History* (New York & London: Verso Books)

Weekes-Barnard, D. (1997) 'Shades of Blackness: Young Black female constructions of beauty', in H. S. Mirza (ed.), *Black British Feminism: A Reader* (London & New York: Routledge)

Women and Equalities Committee (2019) *The Use of Non-Disclosure Agreements in Discrimination Cases*, Ninth Report of Session 2017–2019 (London: House of Commons)

Wood, M., Hales, J., Purdon, S., Sejersen, T. & Hayllar, O. (2009) *A Test for Racial Discrimination in Recruitment Practice in British Cities*, Research Report 607 (London: Department for Work & Pensions)

Youde, K. (2019) 'Younis leaves Southbank after less than a year', *Arts Professional*, 25 October

Young, I. M. (2011) *Justice and the Politics of Difference* (Princeton & Oxford: Princeton University Press)

Young, S. (2020) 'Black History Month: Royal Mail unveils special boxes in honour of Black Britons', *The Independent*, Wednesday 30 September

Younge, G. (2018) 'Boris Johnson's white privilege: Imagine he was a Black woman', *The Guardian*, Friday 2 March

Acknowledgements

While the plans for this book began long before the global pandemic struck, much of the writing took place during it and while I was going through some difficult health and professional challenges. There are many people I would like to thank for their time, energy and support at pivotal moments during this period. Alvaro and Chiara, I deeply appreciate the gift of your beachside apartment while I finished drafting the proposal for this book. The sunrises and sunsets were breathtaking. Chidi Iweha helped me stay sane through a difficult work-related situation; Stephanie Brobbey cared for me during a period of ill health and is an all-round fabulous dahling; and Ronnie McCalla checked in with regularity and without hesitation.

There are many who either shaped my thinking or influenced and humbled me with their tenacity and wisdom. I must thank the original Runnymede 'massive' Michelynn Lafleche, Dr Debbie Weekes-Barnard, Dr Omar Khan, Sarah Isal (now Williamson), Filz Caran and Qaisra Khan with whom I shared the early part of my career. Runnymede was – and remains – one of the few places I could genuinely take my full self to work and where pleasures of both the mind and the stomach were deliciously satiated. Who could ask for more? There are others: Professor Ann Phoenix, Professor Gus John and Baroness Doreen Lawrence. I remain amazed at their resolve. I must, of course, give a shout out to the Black female professors who took part so generously in my research and the exhibition that followed and offer special, gold-plated thanks to Professor Cynthia Pine and Professor Funmi Olonisakin.

My academic identity was forged many years ago at what was then the Institute of Education (long before it merged with UCL). I grew and read so much during that time. I came to learn the backstreets of Bloomsbury, indulged in wonderful debates and, when my limited funds allowed, shared food and drinks into the evening. Recalling those times, I must give personal thanks to Professor David Gillborn who has walked with me throughout much of my professional journey and copes with my incessant interrogations about almost every subject known to humankind. And though he is no longer with us, I am indebted to Professor Geoff Whitty who graciously indulged my many curiosities about the workings of academia, and to Professor Gemma Morris who encouraged me to own my academic achievements and my unique way of thinking even if the academy said differently.

There are many scholars in the US who continue to inspire and have offered words of guidance including Professor Gloria Ladson-Billings and Professor Kimberlé Crenshaw. They embody wisdom, community and groundedness in a way we are often too hesitant to do in the UK. Professor Michael Apple, Professor Adrienne Dixson and Professor Jerlando Jackson hosted me with generosity during my scholarly visits to their institutions in the US. And I must thank the scholars of colour who attended the annual American Educational Research Association conferences. I cannot begin to express how this Black British academic was affirmed by bearing witness to such an amazing array of scholars who wowed with their intellectual argument by day and, by night, got on down at the Black and Brown ball. Being in their presence fed and nourished my soul and kept me going – at least for a while – when I returned to the grey academic landscape of the UK.

Finally, I must thank my literary agent Carrie Plitt as well as Casiana Ionita and the rest of the Penguin Press team for their warmth, guidance and support throughout.